FINDING
MYSELF
FROM THE
OUTSIDE IN

FINDING MYSELF

FROM THE

OUTSIDE IN

Beating depression
and debuting as a
fitness model at 46!

Jane Curnow

March 2016

ISBN: 978-0-646-95389-2

Finding Myself from the Inside Out

The content of this book is for general instruction only. Each person's physical, emotional, and spiritual condition is unique. The instruction in this book is not intended to replace or interrupt the reader's relationship with a physician or other health professional. Please consult your doctor for matters pertaining to your specific health and diet.

To contact the publisher, visit www.createspace.com

To contact the author, visit www.janecurnow.com

Cover design by Christian Fuenfhausen, CEF Design
www.cefdesign.com
Interior design by Heather McIntyre, Cover&Layout
www.coverandlayout.com
Edited by Amy Harke-Moore, The Write Helper
www.thewritehelper.com

Printed in the United States of America

This book is dedicated to my mother,
Elizabeth.

9 April 1939 – 29 November 2010

I feel you with me and
I am so happy we are at peace.

Acknowledgements

Unlike most books you will read, I don't have a tribe of family behind me supporting me to thank, which is one of the main reasons this book has come about! So much of my journey has been on my own which has only made me stronger and wiser. I have spent a lifetime resenting that I didn't have the family or partner to support me, and yet their absence has fuelled my success and transformation.

My first thank-you must go to a very special lifelong friend who actually is my second husband, Wayne Miranda. I seriously would not be alive today if it wasn't for this man. He has seen me at my very lowest and was the only one, on numerous occasions, to extend a hand to help me through. Clearly we were never meant to be husband and wife, but we have a brother-sister relationship that I am eternally grateful for. He has provided stability and unconditional love, advice and guidance; he has taught me the meaning of loyalty, integrity, humility and honesty and has been an incredible role model. He has shaped me into a better human being. Thank you just doesn't seem enough to express my gratitude.

The next man to have a profound influence on me is my trainer and coach from the beginning of my bodybuilding journey, Tom Hewett. The title personal trainer doesn't come close to describing the role he has played in my transformation. My mentor, coach, friend—I attribute my transformation not just physically but spiritually and my recovery from depression (that he wasn't even aware of!) due to his support and faith in me. The universe was truly steering me in the right direction when this incredible man was delivered to my life. Thanks Tommy!

And yet another man who I must thank for being instrumental in guiding me through my transformation, Luke Britton. Again, the title physiotherapist doesn't come close to describing the positive influence and guidance he has provided me. From navigating me through my serious injuries to full recovery, to ongoing maintenance to ensure my body is in peak condition to train to the level that I do, to his compassion of my tears and emotion, to his advice and guidance through my steep learning curve of the bodybuilding and fitness industry, to his support of me pursuing my dreams. Thanks Luke!

Thanks also to Joshua Rothenthal, the founder and director of the Institute of Integrative Nutrition®. A man I have never met, but who has inspired me to be a part of his wellness movement to change the health of the world. I am truly honoured to be a loyal member and follower.

Thanks to the friends who sit on the peripheral of my wellness life but contribute to my wellbeing to enable me to follow my dreams: Tina Jones, Kate Duffy and Anthony Freijy. And to the numerous mentors who have touched my life along the way: Kira Sutherland, Julie Rice, Nicole Rigato, Debbie Spellman, Jacquie Prydie, Donna Bourne and Dr Ellen Campion. All incredible women who have inspired and supported me.

Thanks also to my publishing team that have not only been patient with a rookie author but have provided education and support that I am beyond grateful for: Amy Harke-Moore from The Write Helper, Christian Fuenfhausen from CEF Design and Heather McIntyre from Cover&Layout. And to all the team from the Launch Your Dream Book Course for incredible support and guidance!

And a special thank you to my past, current and future clients. Your belief in me has given me the strength and motivation to continue pursuing my dream. I have learnt so much from you all, and watching you transform your lives is the most incredible gift. I am beyond blessed to be a part of your journey, and my greatest reward is seeing you so happy, healthy and strong.

FINDING MYSELF

FROM THE

OUTSIDE IN

Table of Contents

Introduction

So here I am on the brink of my half century and looking and feeling younger, happier, healthier and sexier than ever! As I write this, my goal is to compete again shortly after my fiftieth birthday. Wow! If you had said to me even five years ago that I would be getting up on stage in a bikini to celebrate my fiftieth, I would have thought you were hallucinating! How on earth did I end up here??!!! I have to pinch myself as my life certainly hasn't gone to my original plan, and I very nearly didn't make it this far!

I have feared getting older my entire life. I have obsessed about my weight and appearance my entire life. I made it my soul purpose to "do" life in the order we are supposed to; man, marry, house, kids. And I have suffered from depression my entire life! I have always wondered who writes these rules that society places on women. Why is it we feel so much pressure to be beautiful, to be slim, to be married, to be a mother, to be everything to everyone—to be perfect! In the post women's liberation era, there still exists this incredible pressure, and I am always stunned when I still hear young, single women talk about the necessity to find a man, to settle down (and in too many cases this actually means to settle...) to have children as well as have the perfect body. We are expecting ourselves to be super human! I also hear young married women frown upon and put down their single friends; why is that? Are we incomplete without a man? These pressures have been the main cause of my depression (which I was very aware of) coupled with my low self-esteem (which I had no awareness of) caused by a difficult childhood and less than ideal parental role models.

This is a book about my transformational journey, and I don't just mean in the physical sense. I have spent a lifetime hating myself, my body, my life! I always felt something wasn't right with me, and I have searched and searched, spent thousands and thousands trying to "fix" myself without ever being able to articulate what it was I was trying to fix! I would blame my mother, father, their divorce, my stepfather, relationships, childhood. Surely it wasn't my fault...? I have tried every book, pill, therapist, healer, course and diet. I have changed jobs, partners, cities and homes, thinking, surely the next chapter will be the happy one. Bodybuilding was yet another attempt—maybe if I achieve the perfect body and show it off on stage, finally I will be happy?

The funny thing about my journey is that I can look back over the years to the many people and books I turned to for help, and most of these tools were given to me. I just wasn't ready to recognise them or put them into regular practise. I had to go to the incredible extreme of competing as a fitness model which required an almighty effort to get this self-loathing, shy, introverted, broken—addicted to anything that I could get my hands on girl—strutting in a bikini on stage. Was I insane?!!

So here I am, and, yes, my new addiction is weight lifting if you were wondering! But the byproduct of my journey to stage was that I had to start to take care of my body. I had to give up the partying, be strict with my diet and get plenty of sleep. I was introduced to a whole new world that included new mentors, and I really had to dig deep to get this broken girl on stage. And I am not for one second recommending you do that! But it was this journey that finally saw me gain self-respect, which is beyond ironic as I now know it was my vanity and low self-esteem that drove me down this path.

This is not a book about bodybuilding. Extreme fitness was the catalyst for my change; however, this is not for everyone! The principles I am about to share with you that I have used to transform my life are applicable to all and in any circumstance. There will, of course, be plenty of focus on health, but I am not for one second suggesting that you start pumping iron! But if this does resonate with you, I would love to hear from you. ☺

I have written this book for the same reasons I am beyond passionate about coaching women. To fast-track your journey to self-love, self-acceptance and better health. To mend that broken heart if you have one, increase your energy, have you looking and feeling younger, sexier, happier, and empower you to be the best you can be. And to find that lost mojo that women seem to trade in for the sake of following the rules of society. It doesn't have to be that way! Life is too short to not live every day with passion and purpose; I spent 46 years being miserable. What a waste!

I have split this book into two halves: body and mind. Most would say to achieve the body you want it all starts in the mind; most would say that mental strength comes first before competing in the bodybuilding world or undertaking any sort of physical transformation. But I am not sure that many start out this way. Many women struggle to lose the weight when there are still mental or emotional blockages of some sort. This is where my genetics have helped me; I achieved the body with a broken heart and mind. My mental strength and spiritual transformation was born out of achieving premium health and physical strength. There is no doubt that the body and mind are intrinsically connected, and we are all very different, so if you feel it is your mind that needs the work first, feel free to start with that section.

Thank you for choosing my book; I am truly honored. There are millions of books out there, and I am incredibly grateful that you have chosen to pick up mine and hopefully learn a few things from my journey. Whatever we want to achieve in life, there is usually someone out there who has done it or is doing it. While you may not want to follow every step I have, hopefully I will spark your interest enough to do further research. Take whatever resonates with you to propel you towards your own goals, or join my exclusive coaching program so I can work alongside you. ☺

"I inspire women. I shine a light into their heart and grow their inner goddess. I find their lost mojo and develop their inner sparkle. I am not just a coach, I am the loyal, fanatical fan who leads the cheer squad giving my undying support that will transform into self-support beyond their wildest expectations. Health will be the catalyst for a change in perspective as well as an understanding of the power of premium health and how amazing our body and life is supposed to feel!"

—Jane Curnow
February 2016

AGELESS
BODY

"For countless numbers of years, women have been brainwashed into believing that their body deteriorates when they have children, they have operations, or they reach 30, 40, 50, 60. But really one's body deteriorates because one lets it."

—Doris Barrilleaux
From her book "Forever Fit"
GORGO Women's Fitness Magazine

Ageless Body

My journey begins with tremendous pain. Not the emotional pain that plagued me all my adult life, although this was always simmering under the surface, but physical pain. I had been a cardio bunny-group exercise addict all my life, starting with the Jane Fonda aerobic years in the 80s (yes I wore leg warmers and G-string leotards..... Lol!) Despite all my depression and self-neglect, you would still see me at the gym at least four times a week, jumping up and down like a crazy woman, fuelled by my vanity and obsession to stay slim. Even through my days of bordering on anorexic, barely weighing in at 55 kilograms—I am 175 centimetres tall—I would still be there near fainting. And, yes, even through my partying years it wasn't unusual to see me out until the wee hours and then fronting up to the gym in the morning! I have never vomited at the gym, which always surprised me..

This high impact exercise of 20 plus years had taken its toll, and for the first time at the age of 45 I had a serious injury. I had been very lucky up until then, and in retrospect I wish I hadn't! Little did I know that this injury was going to be responsible for my spiritual awakening, for me finding my life purpose and finally moving past my debilitating depression. But I was going to put up a hell of a fight first!

I have an extremely high tolerance for pain. Not sure how or why this is and I didn't know it up until then. Emotional pain is my downfall so maybe physical pain is easy for me to tolerate. I would have aced childbirth, I tell you! Now my physio is a big muscular guy, and he was pummelling me every week. He was telling me over and over that my training had to change, that my cardio days were over, but I wasn't listening. I didn't recognise myself without my group exercise classes. How was I going to stay slim? Cardio was one of many addictions that plagued my life. So I would endure immense pain both at the hands of my physio every week, in the gym, and eventually in bed as I couldn't sleep on my side which I prefer to do. I got to the point where I had a little episode… with my physio mumbling I told you so… I could barely walk now. The MRI showed a labral tear in my left hip socket, and at my age a hip replacement was not an option—I was too young. The only resolution was a cortisone injection deep into my hip joint, more physio, rehab exercises and resistance training to strengthen the muscles around the hip. Oh, and no more cardio! I was beside myself!

I should clarify my injury here for anyone who is on the group exercise path as I was. A labral tear in the hip socket is certainly from continuous high impact exercises over many, many years; however, if I had included resistance training as well as my cardio sessions I would not have been in this situation. I am not unique when it comes to imbalances in my body, most of us are slightly off centre and have certain weaknesses on either our right or left side, and I am sure most of us have been told that one leg is longer than the other… One of my main issues—there are many—is my right glute muscle fires a millisecond later than the left. If I had been doing weight training to correct these postural issues, which also come from years of desk work, then perhaps I would not have got myself into such a predicament. Hence why I wish this injury had surfaced sooner as I had now reached the point of no return.

So when I say my physio literally dragged me by the hair into the weights room, I am not kidding. I had endured all this pain for over six months, and with the further pain of the cortisone injection and the beyond boring rehab exercises, I would have been stupid to start jumping up and down again. Lifting weights (or swimming) was the only form of exercise left available to me, and I had to accept it.

The weights room is not much of a place for a girl; it's intimidating! I hadn't a clue what to do, and what was the fuss about ensuring I had correct form? I felt uncomfortable with all those meaty guys around me. Everyone seems to know what they were doing, and I was paranoid about making a fool of myself. I was just too used to an instructor telling me what to do in the gym, so I could see that if I was going to take up this new form of exercise, I needed a trainer to teach me.

After yet another painful session with my physio, coupled with another lecture of what training I should be doing, I was bored at work and started googling as you do. Wasn't weight training what fitness models do? I figured if I was going to give up the whole group exercise thing that maybe a change in gyms was on the cards. So my first Google search was "how to become a fitness model". The first result of my search was a new gym a few blocks from my office that specialised in training fitness models and the popular 12 week transformation packages. It had only been open two days! I rang and made an appointment, and the rest, as they say, is history. This broken, vain girl was on her way to a new life!

I describe the physical side of my transformation first because my journey started here, on the outside. At the age of 45 I had no real clue as to what my emotional issues were, despite years and years of therapy, and I certainly didn't undertake the change in my gym routine with any other motivation than necessity, in a physical sense, due to injury, my vanity, and this vague thought that maybe I could compete. Then maybe I would finally be happier with life. I had just come through some major depressive episodes in recent years, trying to deal with the realisation that I had missed out on having children, plus the suspicious death of my mother. The timing couldn't have been more perfect in retrospect; however, I just want to make it clear at this point that my motivation was purely aesthetic and for all the wrong reasons!

A funny thing happens when you start nurturing your body with the right fuel and you become physically strong through lifting heavy weights. When you clean up your diet, sleep more, drink more water and follow a disciplined routine. When you give up the partying, self-neglect and disrespectful behaviour. The most empowering feelings started to come over me. It didn't happen overnight, and it didn't happen consciously. It didn't come forth into my awareness until I was well past my second competition. I got all the way to stage before I realised that having the perfect female body, strutting around on stage in a bikini was not the answer to my unhappiness. But with this journey to stage I had started a number of mind techniques that I cover in the second half of the book. My mind and body were on a transformational journey that continues to this very day. My attempt at the ultimate display of vanity led me to the answers I had been searching for my entire life. I find it so ironic that this aesthetic sport has given me the self-respect I never had.

> *"As I improved my diet I started*
> *to learn to love myself,*
> *probably for the first time ever."*
> *—Frank Ferrante*
> *Hungry for Change, FMTV.*

This quote sums up my journey. I now strongly believe and understand that the key to overcoming any emotional challenge in life is premium health. Once you take care of your body on the outside and make it healthy and strong, your mind will follow on the inside. Not only that, I have watched and felt the reversal of aging damage to my body and mind as well. The body and mind are intricately connected; you will not find any successful person who does not have some form of health routine. And this is why I believe that health coaching is the way of the future. Life or career coaching will only get you so far; if you don't address health and weight issues, it is difficult to succeed in any area of your life. Health coaches will soon become a recognised profession in the US thanks to my college, the Institute of Integrative Nutrition®. And as with all things American, Australia will follow. I am so very proud to be a part of this movement.

And so we begin with creating an ageless body.... ☺

"To keep the body in good health is a duty... otherwise, we shall not be able to keep our mind strong and clear."
—Buddha

Finding Myself from the Outside In

Protein –
the Building
Blocks of Life

I didn't have a clue. Wasn't protein just for guys? I hadn't been educated in school about the essential nutrients our bodies need, nor had I bothered to do my own study since. Like most, my education on nutrition consisted of what the marketers chose to tell me through advertising and my own ignorant perception that protein was just for meat heads. Didn't protein make you big and strong? I didn't think as a girl I needed to be either.

As I wasn't a fan of cooking, I wasn't a big eater, and as I was perpetually undereating, with a big binge on the weekend, protein was not a big part of my diet. Chicken at a push but not much red meat at all.

I will never forget when I was sent my first nutrition plan; I nearly died! Red meat and nuts for breakfast? Was my coach insane? And what's this five meals a day rubbish?!!! And meat with every meal! What the hell was I thinking paying all that money for this new gym?! I didn't sign up for this!

But I had signed up. I had paid a lot of money, and my vanity was surging through my veins. I had to do it! For a long time I just did what I was told. I had faith in my coach and trainer. I could see the results of their expertise all around me in the gym, and indeed their own physiques were impressive. If you want the body, eat the meat!

It wasn't until after my first competition when I started studying nutrition myself that it all fell into place. Six months in to this new way of life and I had now started to feel the effects of premium health. I hadn't become a meat head nor had I become fat. In fact, my body looked the best it ever had! Maybe there was something to this weird diet I was on...

What is Protein?

Protein is an essential part of every living organism and is therefore a vital component of a healthy diet. The word protein actually comes from the Greek word protos which means first rank or position, in recognition of how important protein is to life.

The protein that you eat (and the protein in your body) is made up of smaller molecules called amino acids. Amino acids are the building blocks of protein because these smaller molecules are assembled in various ways to build protein. The body needs twenty amino acids in order to build protein, eleven of which it can create or synthesize on its own, however, the remaining nine, called essential amino acids, must be obtained through the food we eat. Why do we need so many? Because the sequence of these amino acids determines specifically what that protein is and does—build muscle, nerves, hair, nails and more.

Protein is essential to all bodily functions. This is why it is called the body's building blocks as every cell and every organ is built from protein.

The Protein You Eat

Have you ever thought about the differences in the protein-rich food you eat? An egg for example has a different sequence of amino acids than, say, a glass of milk or a piece of steak. So when you are eating different forms of protein sources you are eating different amino acids. For example, when you have milk or yoghurt you are eating proteins called casein and whey. When you have meat, fish or poultry you would be eating collagen and myosin, among others. This is why it is so important to eat a variety of different protein sources.

Each of these different sequences of amino acids, once digested and absorbed, can be used as building blocks for the protein required throughout your body.

You Need Protein Daily

Eating the right amount and the right type of protein every day is therefore really important! If you are consistently running on a shortage of protein, your body will have no choice but to start breaking down protein within your body to provide the amino acids to produce the most vital protein.

This is why it is so critical for building muscle that protein is consumed every few hours to ensure the body doesn't start breaking down my hard-earned muscle for more vital needs throughout the body. Plus eating protein regularly keeps me feeling full.

Types of Protein

Proteins that come from animal sources contain all of the essential amino acids. So meat, fish, poultry, eggs and milk products are called complete protein.

Plant protein is found in beans, lentils, nuts and whole grains and are lacking one or more essential amino acids, so they are considered incomplete. (Soybeans and foods derived from soy are an exception.) This is why it is important for vegetarians to incorporate a wide variety of foods in their diet.

On the following pages are lists of protein sources both for vegetarian and meat-eating lifestyles.

Vegan Sources of Protein

Grains   A staple in most cultures around the world but, as with all foods man has interfered with, there is a big difference in the quality. Refined grains such as white flour and white rice have had their bran and germ removed and are stripped of the naturally occurring vitamins, minerals and fibre. Whole grains such as rice, millet, quinoa and oats still contain these nutrient-rich components. Gluten, which is the protein found in wheat, barley and rye, is a hot topic and can cause sensitivities for many who often don't even realise.

Beans   Contain a more complete set of amino acids than other plant foods. For easier digestion, choose fresh beans such as split peas, mung and adzuki beans. You could also try soaking beans overnight, adding spices or vinegar, skimming off cooking foam, pressure cooking or puréeing to improve digestibility.

Soy   Common forms of soybeans include edamame (baby soybeans), tofu (soybean curd), tempeh, miso and tamari (fermented soybeans) and can be difficult to digest. Fermented soy is often the easiest form to digest. Highly processed, unnatural soy like commercial soymilk, soy-meat and soy-ice cream are not recommended. Soybeans are one of the most genetically modified crops, so it is important to choose organic whenever possible.

Nuts   Generally considered a fat, not a protein. Peanuts, which are actually legumes, are far higher in protein than any nut. Nuts contain heart-healthy mono-unsaturated fats and antioxidants. More on this shortly. Go for raw or roasted not salted wherever possible.

Protein bars   Many contain refined carbohydrates, highly processed protein isolates, chemicals, sugar and artificial sweeteners. Unless homemade, protein bars should be avoided.

Protein powder   Whey protein is one of the most easily assimilated forms of protein and is controversial as it is manmade. Check for high-quality ingredients.

Leafy greens   Broccoli, spinach, kale, bok choy, any green leafy lettuce (not iceberg), and watercress all contain varying amounts of protein. Green leafy vegetables are dense with easily-assimilated amino acids as well as other life-extending nutrients.

Animal Sources of Protein

Meat   Chicken, turkey, duck, lamb, beef and others. Try different types to discover what works best with your body. Go for grass-fed, free-range organic wherever possible. Conventionally farmed meat is laden with chemical additives, growth hormones and antibiotics.

Eggs   Quick, practical, inexpensive protein source. Don't be scared of the yolk! High in fat, yes, but it is good fat! More on this shortly. As with meat, and for the same reasons, go for organic wherever possible.

Fish   Fresh is preferable over canned. Beware of mercury poisoning, over-fishing, genetic engineering and added chemicals. Choose wild fish whenever possible.

Dairy   Many people have negative reactions to cows' milk and don't realise it. Try other dairy foods like buttermilk, greek yogurt, white cheeses. Or try other animal species like goat and sheep. Buy organic to avoid growth hormones and antibiotics.

Top Tips

- Aim to include protein with every meal and snack. Protein fills you up and keeps you fuller for longer.
- If you eat meat as your protein source, the healthiest by far is grass-fed, organic or free-range. More on this shortly.
- Meat is best digested when eaten by itself or with salad.
- Cook the meat less and you won't corrupt the amino acids as much.
- Good quality whey protein powder should be on everyone's shopping list. Not only is it easily assimilated by your body, but it is so easy to throw into a smoothie or on top of your yoghurt. And it comes in great flavours!

*"How can you expect your body
to last for a long and enjoyable lifetime
if you don't put the proper building
blocks in there?"*

—Dr Dan Rogers,
Food Matters, FMTV

Fats Don't Make You Fat!

J ust like protein, I didn't have a clue. Surely fat makes you fat—it's fat! Again, I was not educated about this in school and hadn't bothered to do my own research. I grew up in the thick of the "Fat makes you fat" media frenzy of the 80s and 90s, with low fat foods popping up everywhere you looked. And if it was on the news that fat made you fat, then clearly it does!

As a result I avoided all fat at all costs. I had low fat everything from milk to yoghurt to cheese, and I cringe when I realise I got sucked into the low fat margarine craze. After all, butter is pure fat, isn't it? If I did eat meat, I cut off every last morsel of fat and even went so far as when buying a barbecue chicken only eating the breast, as the rest was far too fatty!

So I looked at my new nutrition plan—with nuts, avocado, full cream Greek yoghurt, butter and olive oil with every meal! Huh?! In the early days I was even allowed halloumi cheese! But once again I had invested a lot of time and money into this program—and I wanted that body! So I did as I was told, and, lo and behold, I didn't get fat...

So What's the Skinny on Fat?

It is a common misconception that fats should be eliminated from our diet in order to lose weight. The fact is the body utilises dietary fat for energy; health of hair, skin and nails; vitamin absorption; and many every day bodily functions. Good fats can actually help you lose weight as well as protect you from heart disease, cancer, depression, reduce blood pressure, and lower cholesterol. With today's modern diet the most pervasive form of nutritional deficiency we experience is for essential fatty acids because we are all avoiding fat to lose weight!

The term "essential" means that our bodies have to have the nutrient, and we must obtain it from an outside source. Our bodies can manufacture certain types of fats, but we have to get "essential fatty acids" from the food we eat.

The main types of essential fatty acids that we need on a daily basis are omega-3 and omega-6 in the correct ratio, which very few of our modern diets contain.

With all the conflicting information in the media and when even science seems to contradict which fats are healthy and which are not it's no wonder many people are confused about the types of fats we should be eating, where to find the essential fatty acids, and which types we should be avoiding. Let me briefly explain.

Main types of fats

Saturated

Monounsaturated

Polyunsaturated

Trans-fatty acids

Saturated	Mono-unsaturated	Poly-unsaturated	Trans-fatty acid
Where you'll find them			
Beef, poultry, pork, eggs, full-fat milk, cheese, yoghurt, butter, some coconut oil	Avocados, olives, olive oil, nuts, sunflower oil, seeds, peanut oil, sesame oil, some peanut butters	Salmon, herring, trout, sardines, mackerel, fresh tuna, flax seed, walnuts, soybean oil, flax seed oil, safflower oil, sesame oil, almond butter	Or unsaturated fats. Margarine, processed foods, sweets, chips, pastries, cakes, some peanut butters
What they are			
Solid at room temperature.	Liquid at room temperature but become solid when chilled.	Liquid at room temperature and even when chilled. Known as the "omega fats".	Most are created industrially by adding hydrogen bonds to liquid oils to extend shelf life of processed foods.
Physiologic effects			
Potential increase risk of heart disease. Raise LDL (bad) cholesterol levels.	Raise (good) HDL and lower (bad) LDL cholesterol.	Raise (good) HDL and lower (bad) LDL cholesterol. Omega-3 fatty acids are considered anti-inflammatory and are associated with lower risk of death.	Raise (bad) LDL and lower (good) HDL cholesterol, which leads to plaque buildup in arteries and increased risk of heart disease
What to eat – What to avoid			
Mixed opinions on how much is good or bad for you.	Generally considered heart-healthy, these foods should be eaten daily.	Generally considered heart-healthy, these foods should be eaten as often as possible.	Avoid!

As you can see, the polyunsaturated, rich in omega-3s, is lacking from our modern-day diet. In pre-historic times our diets had far less saturated fat and the ratio of omega-6 to omega-3 was one to one. From the foods listed above, the ratio today is more like twenty to one. This unnatural balance causes inflammation which can also increase the likelihood of your body actually storing fat.

Top Tips

- Include flaxseed oil, which is very rich in omega-3s, in salad dressings or smoothies. But do not cook in flaxseed oil as it becomes rancid when exposed to heat. Ground flaxseeds (linseeds) are excellent also; however, as soon as they are ground the oil starts becoming rancid so it is best to buy them whole and grind your own.
- Eat more cold-water fish but the less cooking the better. (Bake or grill) If you fry, you will have little or no useable omega-3s left.
- Eat organic meat and dairy from grass-fed animals. If the animal is not grass-fed, then the fat is mainly saturated fat, not essential fat.
- Use omega-3 enriched eggs. These are eggs that are produced by chickens that have been fed flaxseeds. Boiled eggs have more uncorrupted omega-3s than fried eggs because the temperature of the boiling water is lower. Go for boiled or scrambled over fried.
- Include avocados, olive oil, nuts and seeds in your daily diet.
- Supplement your diet with 5-10 grams of omega-3 every day. (Fish or krill oil)

- If you are buying "fat free" products read the ingredient list. You will find chemical additives and sugar! These products have been stripped of their naturally occurring essential fatty acids. A better option is the full fat product.

"It is not fat that makes you fat.
It's sugar!"
—Dr Christine Northrup
Hungry for Change, FMTV

Finding Myself from the Outside In

Why Are Carbs
So Scary?

As with protein and fat, I had no formal education in school, nor did I do any research of my own. I was completely influenced by the media and advertising. *Carbs make you fat, don't they? Wasn't that what Dr Atkins was on about?* But hang on a minute—his recommendation was high fat!

Anybody else confused? And what is a carb anyway? I thought carbs were anything that was not meat or vegetables—bread, pasta, rice.

The carb factor in my new nutrition plan didn't bother me so much as I was well-conditioned in the "carbs make you fat" school of thought, and I had minimal carbs in the beginning. (Later on in the muscle-building phase was a different story!) And I still struggle to this day with eating a lot of carbs; it truly is a psychological belief that has been drummed into us by very clever marketers.

The key with carbs, just like with fats, there are good and bad carbs. I was allowed brown rice, sweet potato, oats and quinoa. *What the hell is quinoa?*

What is a Carb?
Carbohydrates get a lot of bad press, but it is just a matter of knowing which are the good ones and which ones you should avoid.

Refined/Processed Carbohydrate
These are the carbohydrate sources that are a far cry from their original state, and man has stripped them of their fibre and nutrients. White bread, white rice, white pasta, noodles, white sugar are all examples. As there is limited fibre in these

foods, they breakdown very quickly and leave you feeling hungry soon after your meal. They are also high on the glycemic index, which causes glucose and insulin levels to surge. More on this shortly.

Complex "Quality" Carbohydrate

These are carbohydrate sources that are as close to their original state as possible. Steel-cut oats, brown rice, quinoa, millet, barley, sweet potato and sprouted bread are examples. Vegetables and fruit are also considered a carbohydrate and fall into the "quality" section; however, for the purposes of this discussion I am talking about grains. As these carbohydrates contain fibre, this helps slow down digestion, gives you access to energy and nutrients at a rate your body can use and will ensure you feel fuller for longer. They are, therefore, low on the glycemic index, which produces a manageable response to insulin secretion.

How Do They Affect Your Body?

The preferred fuel source of the body is glucose, which most carbohydrates break down into during digestion. So, in effect, carbohydrates turn into simple sugars and is the sugar in "blood sugar". Compared to protein and fat, carbohydrates burn more quickly, are easily accessible energy and they are used to replenish the backup fuel supplies. However, depending on the carbohydrate consumed, your cells can't keep up with the rising tide of blood sugar unless they get some help. This is where the hormone insulin comes in. Insulin plays many roles in the body, but one critical role is to keep blood sugar under control as well as to get energy to cells. You start secreting insulin, from the pancreas, even before you start eating and without any conscious thought on your behalf. Insulin is preparing your body for the meal you are about to eat. Depending on what you eat, more and more insulin will be secreted to cope with the flooding of glucose into circulation.

The insulin signals muscle, liver and fat cells throughout the body to take up the glucose—and fat if it is available—and remove it from the blood. This is a normal process as elevated blood sugar is toxic to the body. With a moderate amount of the low GI carbs consumed each day, the pancreas can gently say to the muscle, liver and fat cells "please grab that sugar." The pancreas is happy as it doesn't have to scream to get the message across. The muscle, liver and fat cells are happy as they have got room to store moderate amounts of glucose. You are happy as you have consistent energy levels throughout the day as well as staying lean—no mid-afternoon energy slump!

Over time, if excessive amounts of high GI carbohydrates are consumed, the muscle and liver cells stop listening to the pancreas' release of insulin, which is called insulin resistance. The liver and muscle cells that have limited capacity to store glucose shut up shop, and it all gets sent to your fat cells. Hence you put on weight!

As the years go by and excessive "bad" carbohydrate consumption continues, blood sugar levels get higher and higher. The pancreas continues to yell at the fat cells by releasing more and more insulin, but no one is listening and eventually blood sugar levels get to a certain level where Type 2 diabetes is diagnosed. And you are getting fatter and fatter!

So the takeaway from this chemistry lesson is that insulin increases the storage of fat in your fat cells, and it also prevents the cells from releasing it for energy.

Top Tips

- If you really want to lose weight, cutting carbs altogether will get you results more quickly. (I am not including fruits and vegetables in this statement) however, this is not a long term solution. Your body needs carbs!
- Try and improve your carb choices one at a time. Replace white potato with sweet potato.

Weetbix or any commercial cereal with oats—not instant or quick oats, as they are full of sugar! As is all commercial cereal, read your ingredient list. White or whole meal bread with sprouted bread. White rice with brown rice.

- Quinoa is a special favourite as it also contains protein. When cooked properly it really looks and tastes like couscous. Be adventurous and give it a go.
- Invest in a rice cooker; it's so much easier to cook brown rice and quinoa!
- Limit white sugar and all associated sweets, lollies and soft drinks as much as possible. Fruit is not something that is in my diet due to the sugar content, but if you are trying to give up refined sugar, replace it with fruit. At least there is nutritional value in fruit! Best option is berries.
- I have not gone into detail on vegetables, which are also quality carbohydrates, as there is no confusion or debate on their nutritional value. I would encourage you to eat as wider variety as possible in unlimited quantities!

"You can be eating until your heart's content but as long as you are starving on a nutritional basis your body will stay hungry to get those specific nutrients."

—Jon Gabriel
Hungry for Change, FMTV

H$_2$O

I didn't like the taste of water. Or maybe it was not that I didn't like the taste of water, but rather that soft drinks, fruit juices and adding cordial (sugar flavoring) to water was far more enjoyable. I can remember being very proud of myself that I gave up the soft drinks and traded that in for diet cordial. Surely if it is diet and low calorie it is better for me? When you look at me now, it is hard to believe I ever thought that! But like everything else, I believed the marketing on the labels and what the media chose to tell me.

I would drink water when I was exercising—that was all that was in the water fountain at the gym! But in addition to that, I was lucky if I had two glasses a day.

I had been introduced to the importance of water by a naturopath who explained that every cell is made up of 70 percent water, and if I wasn't replenishing that water all my cells would end up looking like sultanas (raisins). Good analogy! But I wasn't listening. I couldn't work out why, whenever I went to see her, I was offered a glass of water. Not really offered—given! The same when I went to my energetic healer or any of my alternate therapists. A glass of water was how every session commenced. (More on alternate therapists in the second half of the book).

My first nutrition plan stated at least two litres of water a day, preferably three. And once again I thought my coach was crazy! I would be on the toilet constantly, wouldn't I? How was I going to achieve that without jumping up and down from my desk dozens of times a day to get more water and go to the bathroom?

What is Water?

The definition of water is it is a colourless, transparent, odorless liquid which forms the seas, lakes, rivers and rain and is the basis of fluids in all living organisms. It is one of the most important substances on earth. Every plant and animal must have water to survive. If there is no water, there is no life.

Water covers over 70 percent of the planet and our bodies are at least 70 percent water also. Most of us would only last three days before dying of thirst. And yet we can go three weeks without food. So it really is no surprise that how much water you drink affects your health.

It is estimated that as much as 75 percent of the population is in a state of chronic dehydration. Chronic dehydration is a form of stress that can cause your body to store additional fat. We often mistake hunger for thirst and eat when we really just need a glass of water. Dehydration can also manifest as cravings for sweets and soft drinks, the very things we are trying to avoid!

How Much Should You Drink?

Too much water can result in mineral imbalances, while too little can cause dehydration, headaches or fatigue. So, how much should you drink? Bio-individuality applies not only to food but also to the amount of water our bodies need to function properly. On average, men should have about three litres and women about two litres of water each day. In order to satisfy individual needs, various lifestyle factors need to be taken into consideration. For example, the water content in fresh fruits and green leafy vegetables may increase hydration in the body.

Water intake should be increased in the following situations:

- Hot or humid temperature
- High altitude (above 8,200 feet)
- High exercise level
- Illness of fever, diarrhea, vomiting

- Infections of the bladder or urinary tract
- Pregnancy and breast feeding
- Alcohol intake
- When trying to lose weight to flush out waste products that accumulate in the fat burning process.

What is the Best Type of Water?

There are many types of water, and once again, it can be misleading as to what is the best source. Not everybody has access to the best sources of water.

Tap water may not always be the safest option. Some cities have very good purification systems, while others leave traces of chlorinated by-products, lead and sometimes bacteria. Chlorinated water kills the friendly bacteria in your stomach. Recent research also indicates that fluoride, which has been in our water supply since the 1970s, is now toxic. (There is actually a huge debate on this, so do educate yourself on fluoride) Research your city's water supply to see if additional home purification is warranted.

Water filters can help to remove contaminants however it is important to know which contaminants are present in your water in order to choose the right filter.

Distillation, which means boiling the water, has also been found to remove impurities and toxins. However, it also removes all traces of beneficial minerals and becomes "dead" water.

Bottled water has become a popular option however, there are growing concerns about chemicals from the plastic seeping into the water (particularly when exposed to sunlight), as well as the effects that the increasing number of bottles having to be disposed is having on the environment.

Water ionizers are gaining more recognition for their ability to create alkaline ionized water through electrolysis, which may have certain health benefits.

Top Tips

- Aim for at least two litres of water a day. Buy a big jug and have it on your desk and make sure it is all gone before you leave for the day.
- Invest in an attractive water bottle accessory for your handbag so you have water with you wherever you go.
- Whenever you feel hungry or have a craving, try a big glass of water first and see if the craving subsides.
- Drink a big glass of water before every meal to fill you up so you eat less.
- Drink two glasses of water first thing in the morning, after your lemon juice in warm water, to thoroughly cleanse your body before your day begins.
- Drink ice cold water. Your body will burn additional calories just getting the water to a normal temperature to digest. It's also good for your complexion.

"Pure water is the world's first and foremost medicine."

—Slovakian Proverb

Zzzzzzz's

Sleep can be such a great escape when you are struggling with life. I used to love going to sleep but always hated those first few seconds on waking—that first millisecond where you are still in that ignorant dream place, but then your conscious mind takes over. All your problems come flooding back and boom—my heart would sink that I had woken up.

I have never been a good sleeper, which goes hand in hand with depression for most. For as long as I can remember, it was always a battle for me to sleep through the night. I always seemed to fall asleep okay but would wake in the early hours and not be able to get back to sleep with the weight of the world over me. Some people who suffer from depression sleep too much; my monkey mind never seemed to give me much peace. If you are having trouble sleeping, then lying in bed with just yourself is a really scary experience! No distractions to take you away from the very person you try all day to escape from.

As a result I would stay up late watching the escape box (TV), or I would ensure I had enough to drink or enough pills to knock me out. Weekday mornings were tough for me!

In more recent years I was on a new antidepressant that had a sleeping tablet component, so I was doing a little better than I had. Chemical-fuelled sleep is not ideal, but I was happy to have an escape that was so easy to obtain. I had pushed the limits too far on too many occasions with traditional sleeping tablets.. so this provided a welcome relief and I was able to cope better with a good night's sleep without the hangover!

Enter Bodybuilding

My coach had told me that sleeping was important to my training. That muscles grow and repair while sleeping, as this is when growth hormone is released. He expected me to get at least eight to nine hours of sleep a night. And once again, I thought are you crazy?! Even with the tablets I was lucky to get six hours.

I did let him know that sleeping was not my strength and we started talking about supplements to assist. I was too embarrassed to tell him I was on anti-depressants. Clearly they weren't enough anyway if he wanted more than eight hours and with my track record of pill-popping I was more than happy to add in a few more that didn't require a prescription! I had never bothered to research alternatives to prescription medication; I put all my faith in doctors back then!

Magnesium was the first sup off the rank. Known to reduce anxiety and stress levels, plus it would help with my recovery from training. GABA and melatonin were two more that I included at a later date. I continue on these three to this day to assist with sleep, amongst other things.

Why Do We Need Good Sleep?

The benefits of good sleep are well researched and documented; however, I don't think any of us realise how detrimental lack of, or poor, sleep has on our health and our ability to deal with life. While we all need different amounts of sleep, I am not sure that we place enough priority on a good night's rest to ensure we are healthy. Sleep is often the first thing that is compromised when we find ourselves overscheduled and stressed.

Sleep, just like my nutrition and training, is prioritised accordingly into my schedule. As I am up so early most mornings, I am in bed by eight most nights. And I don't compromise on this as I know it is vital not only for my success in the gym but my ability to deal with life. Plus it is anti-aging!

Here is a quick list of the benefits of good sleep:
- Better Mood. We all know how emotional we get when we are tired, irritable, impatient and moody. Not enough sleep will affect your behaviour.
- Weight loss. Poor sleep is strongly linked to weight gain. Studies show time and time again the link between sleep deprivation and obesity. If you are awake more, you eat more!
- Metabolism. Poor sleep affects hormones that regulate appetite.
- Clearer thinking. Good sleep maximises your problem-solving skills, enhances memory and learning capabilities.
- Physical Performance. Whether you are running around after the kids all day or training in the gym, good sleep is proven to improve your physical stamina.
- Lowers cortisol, the stress hormone. Stress is a silent killer and affects every area of your body and every aspect of your health.
- Keeps your heart healthy.
- Strengthens the immune system.
- Body Repair. Sleep is the time your body repairs itself, from building muscle to fighting illnesses to rebuilding itself as it does constantly.
- Anti-aging. Growth hormone is released exclusively while you sleep.

We all know most of this but for some reason we don't treat sleep with the respect it deserves. A healthy lifestyle is not just about food and exercise; it is about rest too!

Top Tips

- Schedule it. Make it a priority. Put it in your diary that from whatever set time p.m. to set time a.m. You are not available. To anyone!
- Aim for the same time each night and don't sleep in. Get up at the same time, or close to it, even on weekends. (I do sleep in a little past 4.30 on the weekends...) Support your body's natural rhythm, and stick to a regular sleep schedule.
- Switch off the TV or any electronic devices. The bright, artificial light affects your body's ability to produce melatonin, which is what makes you feel sleepy.
- Read. Preferably not on an electronic device. Reading before sleep is an absolute must for me and is the time I use to cover some of the techniques I have in the second half of this book.
- Meditate. Listen to relaxing music. Try deep breathing. Go for an evening walk and watch the sunset. Have a bath.
- Regular exercise. A no brainer!
- No caffeine. No alcohol. No big meals at night. In fact, I don't have any water after six p.m. either to curb the midnight trips to the bathroom.
- My bedroom is part of my sanctuary. It is cool, dark and quiet, and my bed has beautiful sheets and pillows.

"Sleep is the link that binds good nutrition and our bodies together."

—Anon.

Sup It Up

I grew up in an age when supplements were not prevalent either in the media or on the shelves. Food was of better quality than it is today, although nowhere near the quality of my grandparent's era. Once again school didn't educate me as to what essential nutrients our bodies need, and as the manufactured, processed, sugar-laden, manmade food industry was in full swing by the 60s and 70s and marketed incredibly well, I believed that if it was on the shelf to buy, it was safe to eat.

I can remember when the microwave was introduced, which cut down cooking time. It was a revolution. Fast, microwavable dinners just became part of our lives as technology advanced and we had less and less time to cook. I didn't even like cooking, so it suited me!

Two-minute noodles, packet pasta with built-in sauce, frozen ready-made meals—I thought I was being healthy if I had a Lean Cuisine!

So clearly my new nutrition plan is not going to incorporate all of these manmade quick and easy foods! And my supplementation list was not as long as what I take now, but it was still long! I was already taking a good multi-vitamin, antioxidant and fish oil as I had been advised by a naturopath many years ago that they would help my depression.

A Word on Food Quality

Our farmers suffer the same pressure we do to make a living. Fields that used to be saturated in nutrient-rich soil have been farmed over and over and over so the natural minerals have been stripped from the earth. So the farmer adds fertiliser and additives to ensure he can produce his crops. Then there are all the pests. To ensure he can produce a presentable crop, pesticides are sprayed to ward off all the nasties that eat the growing crop. And all these chemicals get washed away into rivers and streams so even when watering these toxins are recycled back into our food. By the time your tomato gets to you it has already been exposed to dozens of chemicals that a mere wash with water is not going to remove. Have you ever thought why organic produce looks so mothy and unappealing compared to ordinary produce?

The meat industry comes under the same pressure, and not only are so many of these animals treated beyond cruelly, they are fed hormones, drugs and antibiotics to ensure they are free from illness and have plenty of meat on them to sell for slaughter. Chickens are four times bigger today compared to the 1940s. Why do you think that is? Why is puberty coming on earlier and earlier in our children? Why are we becoming immune to more and more antibiotics? It's not only due to being over prescribed by doctors; there are antibiotics in our food!

It is difficult to buy all organic produce when you live inner city like I do without it costing the earth. Even at farmers markets they are not all truly organic. The only way for us to have more access to organic food and to encourage farmers to farm more sustainably is for us as consumers to change the way we spend our money. Farmers are only responding to supply and demand.

Our food supply is declining and has been for some years. Activists such as Michael Pollan and Joel Salatin have been lobbying loudly, but unfortunately the dollars attached to the manufactured food industry are very powerful. We must change our ways very soon if we are going to ensure quality food for generations to come.

Importance of Supplementation

It is for all these reasons that I believe supplementation is a must if we are to give our bodies the necessary vitamins and minerals. In addition to what I describe in the Toxic Load chapter, we need supplementation to support our bodies to eliminate the hidden chemicals and toxins in our food. Our poor Stone Age bodies don't have a clue what these foreign substances are.

My suite of supplements changes regularly depending on funding and what my current goals are in the gym. The first four I believe are not negotiable for all of us. The rest are either bodybuilding sups or because my health is worth it!

Remember, this is what works for me. We are all drastically different.

Multi-vitamin
Magnesium
Probiotic
Fish oil
Vitamin D
Glutamine
GABA
Melatonin
Glutathione
Biotin
COQ10
Laminine
Glycine
Leucine
Creatine
BCAAs
Digestive enzymes
Green tea extract

It's also worth pointing out that there is a huge difference in the quality of supplements you see on the shelves. No regulation exists in the supplement industry like there is in the drug industry, and often what is claimed to be in the tablets is not or it is of poor quality, manmade substances. Generally the practitioner-only brands are the only ones I will use, and I advise to steer clear of the commercial brands. And like anything in life, the higher the price tag the better the quality. I know I only want premium quality going into my one model-issued, has to last a life time body! ☺

Top Tips

- The basic four. Consider adding in a good quality multi-vitamin, fish oil, magnesium and probiotic into your daily routine. I could write a whole chapter on the importance of these four basic supplements! In my opinion they are the minimum requirement to ensure premium health given our declining food quality.
- Antioxidant. Consider adding in an antioxidant that will assist your body in the removal of the excessive toxins it is exposed to every day. Of my list, glutathione and green tea extract cover off the antiox requirement.
- Blood work. Consider getting blood work done to test the levels of some of these vital nutrients. I had no clue I was deficient in vitamin D until I had this test. Vitamin D is vital to absorb calcium and critical for bone and teeth health. Now that I limit my sun exposure I need to supplement. More on this later.
- Research. Do some research into one of your own ailments and what natural alternatives are out there rather than just accepting another prescription from your doctor. Take a more natural approach to your health and only use medicine as a last resort rather than the other way around. Taking on drugs increases your toxic load tenfold and only masks symptoms rather than resolving the underlying cause.

"With nutritionally-depleted foods, chemical additives and our tendency to rely upon pharmaceutical drugs to treat what's wrong with our malnourished bodies, it's no wonder that modern society is getting sicker."

—*Food Matters*, FMTV

Superfood Savvy

What is a superfood? The only one I could name was broccoli, which I didn't like anyway! And like all the previous chapters I didn't have the education nor had I bothered to research.

My bodybuilding journey was never specific about superfoods, but obviously many were included in my nutrition plan. It wasn't until I studied through the Institute of Integrative Nutrition® that I was exposed more to this superfood idea, and I started experimenting and adding in the ones that I liked and that complimented my fitness goals.

What are Superfoods?

The definition of a superfood is a nutrient-rich food considered to be especially beneficial for health and well-being. This is in comparison to common food. Admittedly, the definition is very open ended, and every nutritionist, dietician or health food expert will have a different opinion as to which foods in particular fall into the superfood category. Some experts would argue that there is no food category called superfood! If you google superfoods, you will get a wide variety of different lists, and, it seems, these lists do change according to the latest research or focus from mainstream media. However, the majority are plant based, which is interesting, and although I will never be a vegan or a vegetarian, there is tremendous value in looking at the benefits of these lifestyles.

As the term superfood seems to have been derived for marketing purposes and there is no scientifically backed list, it is important to recognise that some advertising campaigns may use this label to persuade you to buy their product. I noticed one on TV recently for a famous brand of instant porridge that claimed to be a superfood, and, yes, some experts may include oatmeal as a superfood, but I doubt the sugar laced through it would be considered to complement the superfood. Always read your labels and do your own research.

I could argue that everything I eat is a superfood! I rather use the term whole food for my diet. Whole food is basically any food in its whole form, fresh from the farm without interference from man. So nothing in a packet, jar, bottle, bag or box.

But as the superfood buzz word is so popular, the following list is what I consider to be superfoods and what I incorporate into my daily diet. I don't need to mention that this is all organic. ☺

Raw cacao
Maca powder
Aloe Vera juice (not drink)
Oats
Coconut oil
Almonds
Walnuts
Chlorophyll
Spinach
Broccoli
Green tea
Apple cider vinegar (with the mother)
Flax seed oil
Avocado
Eggs (either via supplement or real eggs)
Bone broth
Warm lemon juice
Kefir
Kombucha
Seeds – sesame, pumpkin, fennel, caraway, chia
Sprouts

Some additional ones that you might like to try would be kale, goji berries, blueberries, legumes and garlic.

Top Tips

- Eat for health not just for taste. Back in the Stone Age when we had to either catch or grow our food, I am not sure that we had the luxury of declining food because we didn't like the taste. In this modern age we are spoilt for food options, and while I am not suggesting that you eat food you hate, there are a few on my list that I really don't like the taste of but I down for the sake of my health. Apple cider vinegar is a prime example of one that I gag with, but I still have it every single day due to the enormous health benefits.
- Be creative. Many of these can be slipped into your smoothie or incorporated into your cooking or meals so you can mask the taste. Bone broth is another one I struggle with, so I add it to my mince (ground beef) with dinner, which makes it more like a stew. It enriches the taste without eating the bone broth straight up.
- Research. Just like the supplement tip, consider what ails you personally and have a look at how others have tackled your symptoms through changing up the food they eat. Back in the Stone Age food was the only medicine they had; try some natural alternatives before turning to drugs.

"What we need to be able to do is persuade the public that you are what you eat, food can change your mood, and the choices you make directly affect the outcome of your life."

—Phillip Day
Food Matters, FMTV

Learn to Cook

My mother loved cooking. She also loved entertaining, so she was always experimenting with gourmet dishes. She even took classes to further her culinary skills that were already excellent, and I really didn't understand why she needed to learn more. To say I had the opportunity to learn at home how to cook would be an understatement!

There are many everyday skills that school does not teach you, but cooking was not one of these. I grew up in the Home Economics era, so I also had the opportunity to learn at school. And being born in the 60s, it was very much women's work, and we were expected to cook for our family when we grew up to have our own.

But I wasn't interested. I think I have always had a rebellious streak against "the norm" of what was expected of women. I would rather clean up and do the dishes after my mother had finished cooking than get involved with preparing food. I just didn't see it as something I needed to know.

The 80s saw the introduction of the microwave oven—a revolution in the kitchen. So after I left my childhood home, we could prepare fast food with just a zap in the microwave for five minutes and voila! Dinner was ready! Why on earth would I need to know how to cook?!

Through my twenties I managed to pick a boyfriend or a flatmate who liked to cook, so Jane was always the cleaner, which suited me just fine! I cruised through most of my twenties and thirties either having my meals cooked for me or eating TV dinners. Winning! Or so I thought.

I did manage to put a few meals together when I was married. My husband wasn't a cook, so I had to prepare meals a couple of nights a week. But I never developed the habit of cooking.

Enter Bodybuilding

I keep referring to my shock of my first nutrition plan, and this was another aspect that I was wondering what I had got myself into! All fresh ingredients and forget about any sauce that comes in a packet, jar or bottle for flavour, due to sugar and gluten content. And I was told to throw out my microwave! Blimey, what was I going to eat?!

But once again I had paid a lot of money. And, yes, I had heard by then that any achievements in the gym were 70-80 percent diet... I had to do it, otherwise I would not just be wasting my money but my time.

Food Prep

I had heard this term bandied around the gym, and I could see all the trainers on their breaks in between clients eating out of plastic containers. It didn't take me long to feel the dread that I was going to have to engage in this food prep business on a Sunday afternoon as I certainly couldn't buy my incredibly strict diet from the nearby food court. And I had to prepare for five meals a day!

Fail to Prepare, Prepare to Fail!

We have all heard this quote many times, but I don't think any of us realise the huge impact failing to prepare for the week has on our health and diet. Convenience, processed, manmade, and therefore calorie and chemically-laden, food is everywhere; it's quick and easy—and is your downfall! Our modern day, technological lives have become increasingly hectic and demanding of our time and attention.

Do you remember the wonderful home-cooked meals that your grandmother used to make? Why is it that too many of us have lost this invaluable skill, and, probably more on point, where has the time gone to devote to this, dare I say, boring, domestic chore? Sadly, preparing a healthy, home-cooked family meal has dropped off too many of our priority lists. TV, social media, the Internet, and smart phones are the obvious time suckers!

Food "prep" was a new concept to me when I started down this road. Why on earth would I want to spend my relax time on a Sunday cooking?! But I very quickly realised if I was going to stick to this horrendously strict diet and get my butt on stage, I had to change my approach to food and cooking.

Successful weight loss is 80 percent diet. Another quote that I am sure you have heard of! If you are managing to commit the time to your workouts and you are not making the same commitment in the kitchen, you are wasting your time. You have probably also heard that successful weight loss is not a 12-week diet but a lifestyle change, and your approach to cooking is at the very core of that change.

We must go back to old-style cooking of real food and by pass all the pretend food that comes in a packet, box, bag, jar, bottle, can or container. I am sure you have walked into a fresh food market and been overwhelmed with the sight and smell of all the fresh produce; this is the answer to your weight loss success!

Top Tips

- Buy a week's supply of food on a Friday or Saturday—so one trip to the supermarket per week. Shopping once a week removes the temptation of buying extra naughty food with each trip. Imagine you had to stay back a bit late at work, there is no food in the fridge, and you think I will drop into the supermarket on the way home. There is a huge display of chocolate strategically placed near the checkouts. I have had a hard day. I deserve a treat. Yes, I have been there, too!
- Cook once and eat two, three, four, five times. On Sundays I cook all my protein for the week

(lunch and dinner) so all I have to do is cut up salad or veggies through the week. Some even prep their veggies for the week, but I prefer mine fresh and I don't use a microwave to cook or reheat. Cooked meat lasts for days in the fridge, and for dinner I will reheat (this is usually organic mince). If I run out by the end of the week, eggs are my backup, or I will buy a barbecue chicken.

- If you are a list maker (I am so not!) then write down your meal plan for the week prior to going shopping to ensure you have all the ingredients for the week.
- Prepare your snacks for the week. Nuts, seeds, cut up carrots, celery or cucumber, nut butter, hummus, cottage cheese, dates, rice cakes, fruit, boiled eggs.
- You can even prepare your breakfast smoothies ahead of time; put all the ingredients in a plastic bag and freeze. Then all you need do is throw into the blender frozen, add your liquid base and voila!
- Stock up on plastic containers! of all shapes and sizes. I also have a cooler bag with an ice pack to transport my food, particularly in summer.

Yes, it all takes additional time, organisation and preparation, but isn't your one model-issued, has-to-last-a-lifetime body kinda worth it?

"You don't have to cook fancy or complicated masterpieces. Just good food from fresh ingredients."
—Julia Child
Food Matters, FMTV

Move Your Butt!

As I described in the opening chapter of the body section of this book, I have always been a gym girl. My motivation to exercise was not through love of my body though, but rather through vanity and the constant need to validate myself through my appearance. And, as I mentioned, I was not doing a balance of different types of exercise to ensure longevity of my tendons and joints.

I have been lucky on two occasions now. The first injury you now know about—the labral tear in my left hip socket that sent me kicking and screaming into the weights room. (This injury has all but gone now, by the way) The second and more devastating one was to come and nearly saw the end of my weight lifting days before they had even begun.

Squats are a major part of bodybuilding and a necessity if you want that nice, round peachy butt! Weighted squats were a revelation to me, and like all my new exercises, I loved every minute of it. Like I said, I have a very high tolerance for pain, and it took some months for the awareness of the dull ache in my right knee to come forward into my consciousness. I was attending a weekend workshop on how to be a fitness model only weeks out from my first competition. These weekend boot camps run by my gym are intensive not just on the information side but also on the training side. Six gruelling training sessions over the course of the weekend and let me tell you, they are not for the faint hearted. We were flogged, and I saw a number of girls break down in tears.

A group setting for training is not ideal for me anymore. I push myself to the limit and do whatever the instructor tells me to; after 20 years of exercising this way, it is ingrained in me! But I continue to do exercises that perhaps aren't the greatest for my body, and with my high pain threshold, I rarely feel the pain while I am actually training. On this particular occasion, the pain arrived once I got home and crawled into bed that Saturday night. My right knee was swollen and in agony, but I had just belted myself all weekend, so I wasn't too concerned..

And so began my gradual knee decline. I didn't place in my first competition, and it didn't take much convincing from my trainer to compete again later that year. A decision I made lightly but my knees just weren't going to play. The pain I endured during the preparation for my second competition was more intense than I had ever felt before. I was going to bed every night with ice and painkillers only to be woken in the night with pain once they had worn off. After every leg session I would sit at my desk with ice wrapped around my knees. I was having Epsom salt baths most nights, more painful physio and my training was modified to no more full-range squats, lunges or split squats, but I was still suffering. My physio referred me to a sports physician who administers prolotherapy. This is glucose injected directly into the pain site, which stimulates healing. Well, provided you are not still training, which, of course, I was. I had 10 injections into each knee every other week. To say I was in agony would be an understatement.

The MRI showed irreversible degeneration in both knees with the right being 70 percent gone and the left around 50 percent; they were just about bone on bone. I sought out a highly decorated and well-known sports physician this time. He had been the doctor for Olympic teams, and I was certain he had the answer for me.

Once again my years of high impact without any resistance training to strengthen the right muscles was the cause, but this time there was nowhere left for me to go. Giving up cardio for weights is one thing, but when you are told that you need two knee replacements the game is over. The only form of exercise I would be doing was swimming!

This sports physician said he would help me to stage one more time, but then my career was over. I could have a cortisone injection in each knee a few weeks out from comp. I was more worried about getting a shooting pain on stage than I was of training in pain, so the injections were scheduled. You are only allowed one cortisone injection in each site, and then it would be time to trade in my stage bikini for a pool bikini…

Around the same time as all this happened, a good friend of mine recommended a supplement to me. I was pretty clued up on supplements by this point, and I had a look into it. There are so many out there that claim to perform miracles but I liked the ingredients of this one so I thought why not? I have already lost everything I was open to trying anything.

Cortisone is said to last about six weeks. I had no pain in my last few weeks of training, no pain on stage, and against doctors' advice I continued to train to competition level after competing. And I still do to this very day… The pain never returned! I am on track to compete again in 2016. Pffffft! Swimming my ass!

Does everyone need to be as obsessed as I am?

No! You have to remember that I live the life of an athlete, and while there are many things in my regime that you can incorporate into your life, I am not suggesting for one minute that you pump iron five days a week as I do. Although building more muscle will ensure you speed up your metabolism and burn more calories so I would encourage some weight lifting. It also has numerous other health benefits including improves bone density, lowers blood pressure, lowers the risk of cardiovascular disease, improves immunity and stress levels. Ok so I highly recommend!

However, there is no getting around the fact that if you want to lose weight and improve your health and wellbeing you have to do some form of exercise. It is valuable, not because it burns calories, but because, if done correctly, it can actually make your body change the way it processes and stores fat. From a weight loss perspective, the calories you burn during exercise are only one consideration compared with the many other positive benefits exercise provides. In fact, I would encourage not focusing on the calorie-burning aspect of exercise as it can be discouraging and, in some cases, inaccurate.

At the gym all the cardio equipment supposedly tell you how many calories you are burning. In reality, the machine can't possibly calculate how many calories you have burned since it knows nothing about what's happening at a biochemical level inside your body. The machine is only measuring calories in terms of the mechanical work you are doing based on your age and body weight. This number is truly meaningless, as a body with twice as much muscle might burn twice as many calories or more doing the same exercise. Even if the measure was more accurate, it would be no indication of how much fat you are burning. Do yourself a favour and stop attaching yourself to numbers; the hormonal effect of exercise is far more important than the calories you burn. Let me explain.

Our Stone Age bodies only understand physical stresses and reactions. For your body to change the way it metabolises and stores fat it needs to go into the prehistoric fight or flight mode. Put simply, your body needs to believe you are in grave danger and there is a lion chasing you or you are the one doing the chasing to kill that wild bull to eat! Your body will then understand that the way it currently stores fat—too much of it—could mean the difference between life and death or no dinner!

When you are playing sport and chasing a ball, as you do in soccer, your body assumes you are doing so for one reason only–survival—and it generates the necessary hormonal response in your body. It has no idea what a ball is or that you are voluntarily chasing it. If you are moving that quickly with intense urgency, then your body comes to only one conclusion: you are doing it to stay alive. Why do you think soccer players are always so skinny?

You can take advantage of this hormonal, survival response and exploit it to change the way your body stores fat. You don't have to exercise longer; you just have to exercise smarter!

Top Tips

- Walking is the easiest form of exercise. It is free and does not require any equipment, a gym membership or even transport to get there. Early morning is the best time of day to walk; however, whenever you can fit it into your schedule, lunch hour at work is a great time to rejuvenate you for the afternoon ahead.
- Plan to walk for at least 30 minutes and build up to 60 if you can. Start leisurely and for the majority of the time; however, four to five times during your walk increase your speed for 30 to 60 seconds or until you are short of breath. It is in this time of increased speed that your body will think that its survival is at risk. Try and build up to running intervals, and if you are up for it, incorporate from the get-go.
- This theory can be applied to any exercise— biking, cross trainer, stepper, swimming, dancing or whatever you enjoy.
- Regular exercise will not only improve your physical health, it will help you think more clearly, boost creativity and, most important of all, manage and reduce stress levels. And there is plenty of scientific evidence that proves we live longer and healthier if we exercise regularly.

"Exercise! Like your body is the one thing that is actually yours, something you can mould and transform and never have it be taken away from you. Why would you settle to let your body be anything less than its best?"

—Anon.

Toxic Load

J ust like so many other topics in the body section of this book, I had no idea. Toxins are just air pollution, aren't they? When you grow up surrounded by all these modern-day conveniences, you just assume that everything is safe. That there is someone out there looking out for us, like the government.. Surely we would not be able to consume or use anything that would be detrimental to our health. I didn't think twice about it.

The first time my curiosity was sparked to find out more about toxins was during my preparation for my first competition. My coach was adamant that I needed to have far-infrared saunas a couple of times a week. Not only do these saunas increase your metabolism and blood circulation, relax muscles, reduce stress and burn fat, but they also cleanse and detox the body on a cellular level. After 30 minutes in these hot boxes, my white towel was soaked with black sweat? How was it I was sweating this grey-black substance?

What are toxins?

A toxin is a non-nutritive and potentially harmful molecule, element, organism or energy that your body must either eliminate or store in a safe place until it can be eliminated. Toxins come from our environment in the form of chemicals in our food, water and air as well as medications, electricity and radiation, just to name a few. They come from cosmetics, shampoo, hairspray, deodorant, soaps, moisturizer and tampons as well as cleaning products, air fresheners, fly sprays and other products. (Have you read the ingredient list of all these products?) They are also produced inside your body as a result of cellular mutations and as a natural by-product of your body's metabolic process.

Are you aware that over 3,000 chemicals are added to our food supply? More than 10,000 chemicals are used in the food processing industry. And more than 1,000 chemicals are introduced to industry every year!

These chemicals also "accidently" end up in our ground water, rivers, lakes and oceans as well as deliberately in our food supply. In some parts of the world we are literally swimming in poisons. Frightening!

Our Stone Age bodies are not equipped to deal with space-age poisons. Sometimes, in the body's attempt to neutralize poisons, it may inadvertently create new substances that are even more toxic than the original chemical!

If you are living in a crowded city, eating a modern-day diet, lathering yourself with cosmetics, scrubbing your home with commercial cleaning products, working in an office surrounded by computers, talking on your mobile phone without a hands free and have a Fitbit strapped on your wrist, the toxins may be coming in faster than your body can eliminate them. As a result, all these toxins have to be stored somewhere, and one of the places your body stores them is in your fat cells. It turns out fat cells are a very effective chemical buffer. The fat surrounds the toxin and protects both the fat cell and your body from the potentially damaging effect of the toxin.

Storing toxins in your fat cells is supposed to be a temporary measure. It is a short-term solution until your body can figure out how to eliminate these foreign substances. The problem is that the toxins keep on coming in every day and the backlog to clear keeps getting bigger and bigger. Our Stone Age bodies can't keep up, and rarely does it figure out what to do with these space-age substances.

Toxins can block your body's ability to burn fat, and in one study it is reported that toxins can cause or exacerbate insulin resistance, which is one of the mechanisms of how your body stores fat.

By far the greatest source of toxins in our daily lives is the food we eat. Modern farmed foods are full of poisons, including pesticides, herbicides, artificial flavours, chemical fertilizers. They are also genetically modified. Have you seen the size of strawberries these days! Conventionally farmed, grain-fed meat is even worse because it has all the toxins from the grains plus added hormones and is then chemically treated to look fresh in the supermarket!

Further to this, if we are unable to digest food properly, which is most of us, it will decay in our intestines causing more toxic overload. Most modern foods cause excessive free radicals, which are another form of toxin that needs to be neutralized.

Toxins can also cause inflammation in the body, and many people believe that obesity is actually a disease of inflammation. This is because the hormones involved in inflammation also put your body into fat storage mode.

I hope you are grossed out. You should be!

The Effects of Toxins on the Body

Our bodies are so clever they will keep on working away no matter what you throw at them. But toxicity will slow you down. Maybe you are feeling sluggish or lack energy, feeling tired all the time. Do you struggle with skin problems, aches or pains, allergies, puffy eyes or digestive problems? Do you have a hard time losing weight? These could all be directly related to toxins in your body. This list is almost endless as your body is suffering from chemical overload, and as we are all so different, it can result in a myriad of health complaints. And then we go to the doctor who gives us a pill full of chemicals to mask the symptoms, and our toxic load increases even more.

Top Tips

- Eat more live, fresh, organic fruit and vegetables. Not only are there fewer chemicals, but they contain antioxidants that help neutralize free radicals. They also contain fibre which will help clean out your colon and intestines of undigested food and stagnant waste.

- Eat more organic, grass-fed, free range dairy and meats.
- Drink plenty of filtered water.
- Exercise regularly.
- Have lemon juice with warm water upon rising every day.
- Take two tablespoons of apple cider vinegar a day.
- Limit medication, particularly antibiotics.
- Take a digestive enzyme with meals.
- Take a probiotic every day as well as incorporating more fermented foods into your diet.
- Take an antioxidant supplement every day to support your liver trying to eliminate these toxins.
- Reduce (eliminate!) bad carbs, white sugar and flour, alcohol, caffeine and fried foods.
- Drink green tea.
- Have a far-infrared sauna regularly.
- Have a regular massage.
- Dry brush your skin before your shower each day.
- Rest the organs through fasting or undertaking a detox protocol.
- Have a regular epsom salt bath.

"Our bodies don't know how to digest these 'food like' products, resulting in stress and weight gain! Nourish your body with real foods and it will shine for you."

—Jason Vale

Hungry for Change, FMTV

Vitality

I don't think I have felt "vital" my entire life—up until now! Depression certainly takes the vitality out of you, and since I gave up sunbaking over 10 years ago, I have spent the majority of my time indoors. When I was feeling depressed, the last thing I felt like doing was going outside; curling up indoors was much more my style.

I would spend my entire working week in the office. I only ever went to the gym to exercise, which is also indoors, and then I would be at home depressed all weekend. I went from overexposure to the sun to not seeing the sun at all!

One of the requirements of my gym on commencement down the competing road is a series of blood tests. It's important to get an idea of where the body is at and what is the state of play with hormones and certain nutrients. My vitamin D marker was naturally low, and I was ordered to start going for walks in the sun. I protested, "But I need to protect my skin!" I was told to wear a hat and do it! I was also given vitamin D supplementation due to the critical role this plays in weight loss and general health and wellbeing.

What is vitality?
Vitality is another component to food that our bodies require, and that's the very life force in the food itself. When we are eating "live", biologically active food, we are assimilating the life force of that food—we are assimilating life. If we are assimilating manufactured, dead, manmade, factory-produced food, we are assimilating _____ you fill in the blank!

Many cultures throughout history have acknowledged that a subtle energy surrounds and permeates all living things. This energy has been called many things in different cultures: chi, prana, shakti. In our bodies this energy travels along paths known as meridians in Chinese medicine. If you have ever had acupuncture you will be aware of this.

We can be devitalized not only because we don't have enough life force in our bodies, but also because these meridians can get blocked. Chinese medicine believes that stress, toxins, low-energy thinking and negative emotions cause blockages in the flow of these subtle energies and that these blockages can cause sickness and depression. According to Chinese medicine all disease starts with the blockages of these meridians well before they materialize as a physical ailment.

Blocked energy stagnates and stagnation is devitalisation. Just as stagnant water is less healthy to drink than a flowing stream, the stagnant energy in our bodies is less healthy than free flowing energy. Devitalisation causes stress, which can make us perpetually hungry and tired and can cause our bodies to store excess fat. Because we are exhausted all the time, we crave sugar to boost our energy. We end up eating junk food to simply get us through the day.

We are also likely to get upset more easily, and we become prone to depressing thoughts. Which creates more stress, more negative emotions, more energy blockages and more devitalisation. A vicious cycle!

So how do you unblock these energy pathways? By reducing stress, negative thinking and emotions and also by spending more time in nature. In the space age world we live in, we rarely interact with our natural environment, and yet that is what our Stone Age bodies crave. There is vitality everywhere in nature; sunshine, fresh air, fresh water, the earth, trees and grass all have their own energy that we absorb when we are in their presence. Up until very recently, mankind spent most of our time outdoors interacting with and absorbing the energy flow from nature. Now we spend most of our time indoors, cut off from this nourishing vitality, and, worse, we surround ourselves with electronic devices that omit radioactive waves!

The Vitamin D Connection

There is more and more evidence coming to light that eating live foods and spending time in the sun changes the way our bodies store fat, and this relates to vitamin D.

Studies have shown that raw food vegans, people who only eat live foods, have higher levels of vitamin D. This is credited to the fact that live foods contain the same energetic component that sunlight does, and we convert the subtle energy in live foods into vitamin D, just like with sunlight.

Foods that contain the most vitality are anything live and preferably organic, in season and locally grown. Foods with live chlorophyll have the most vitality, as this is the substance in plants that converts sunlight into nutrients. All types of salads and sprouts are great, the greener the better. The food with the most vitality and live chlorophyll is freshly squeezed wheatgrass juice.

Top Tips

- Eat more live, raw foods, in particular lettuce, kale, spinach, buk choy and wheat grass. Consider adding a green juice to your day.
- Spend a few quiet minutes every day soaking up the sun's rays. You could use this time to do your visualisations and affirmations. More on this in the second half of the book!
- Spend some time in nature every week. A walk in the park at lunchtime. A picnic on the weekend. Take up a hobby that is outdoors.

- Consider a Himalayan Salt Lamp for your home. These lamps improve air quality and increase negative ions, which corrects the imbalance of excessive positive ions. (in this circumstance, positive is not good) negative ions are created naturally by wind, sunlight, surf, waterfalls and thunderstorms. Positive ions are air molecules that have lost their electrons through pollution and electromagnetic waves.

"Nature is the answer. It has the power to restore and revitalise our bodies on the deepest level."

—Kris Carr

Hungry for Change, FMTV

Inhale Exhale

I never thought about my breath or breathing. It is a bodily function run by our subconscious mind, so we never have to think about it. As I was so consumed in my depressing thoughts, I had no clue of the importance of it, and I certainly had no appreciation for it.

During an anxiety attack or when I was at my lowest, sobbing uncontrollably, I can remember whoever had the misfortune of being with me telling me to breathe slowly, take a deep breath. I didn't really think anything of it.

Breathing is an important part of lifting weights, and the timing of the repetition should be around the breath. Like any exercise, when lifting heavy, you do get short of breath. So I was becoming more conscious of my breathing, but it wasn't until I started looking more into meditation that I was awakened to the importance of the breath.

Breath is Life

If you do any form of meditation it is the first thing you are taught. Focus on your breath, feel the air go in through your nostrils, down to your lungs, feel your chest rise and the exhalation out your nostrils again. It's even relaxing just reading that, isn't it? More on this in the second half of the book!

If you have ever had the misfortune to be in an accident where the paramedics have attended or even if you have seen this scene in the movies or on TV, what is the first thing they say to an injured person who is in shock? Take a deep breath. And what is one of the techniques taught to cope with the pain of childbirth? Breathing. When we are in shock, stressed, anxious, angry or any high emotional state, our breathing becomes shallow, cutting off oxygen to the extremities, and is reserved only for our vital organs. Taking a deep breath is the fastest way to calm down your entire system, and yet we spend the majority of our life not even realising this.

There are many benefits from making deep breathing a regular part of your life. Here are a few:

Releases toxins	Your body is designed to eliminate 70 percent of toxins, such as carbon dioxide, through your breath. If you are not breathing effectively, you are not ridding your body of toxins efficiently, and other systems of your body have to work harder, which can lead to illness.
Releases tension	When you are stressed, worried, angry or depressed, everything in your body constricts, and your breathing becomes shallow. Your body is therefore not getting the oxygen in needs.
Relaxes the mind and body	Oxygenation of the brain reduces anxiety levels. As with meditation, if you breathe deeply and not only focus on your breath but on areas of your body that are tight and relax them, you will experience more clarity in your mind.
Relieves pain	What happens when you anticipate pain? You hold your breath. Breathing into your pain helps ease it. My physio is constantly telling me to take a deep breath!
Massages your organs	The movements of your diaphragm during deep breathing massages your stomach, small intestine, liver and pancreas and improves circulation to them.
Strengthens the immune system	Oxygen travels through your body in your bloodstream which is the very site of where your body metabolises nutrients and vitamins.
Improves posture	Good breathing techniques automatically improves your posture as you straighten your torso. Bad posture will encourage more shallow breathing.
Quality of blood	The effective removal of carbon dioxide and the transportation of sufficient oxygen in turn improves the quality of your blood.
Improves digestion and food assimilation	If the stomach receives more oxygen, it operates more efficiently. If food is oxygenated, digestion is improved.

Improves the nervous system	If your brain, spinal cord and nerves receive increased oxygenation, they are more nourished and the communication system in your body is improved.
Strengthens the lungs	Breathing deeply the lungs become more healthy and powerful.
Makes the heart stronger	Breathing deeply reduces the workload on the heart.
Weight control	If you are overweight, the increased oxygen burns excessive fat more efficiently. If you are underweight, the extra oxygen feeds the starving tissues and glands.
Boosts energy and stamina	With all of the previous benefits and the improvement to energy they bring the end result has to be more stamina!
Improves cellular regeneration	As the circulatory system works more efficiently cells can regenerate more efficiently as nutrients are delivered and wastes removed.

It wasn't until I read *Unlimited Power* by Anthony Robbins that I really started paying attention to the importance of breathing. I thought it quite odd that he would have a chapter on breathing until I read a bit more about it. If someone as successful as Anthony Robbins was telling me to deep breathe there must be something to it! He recommends to breathe in a ratio of 1-4-2 for inhale-hold-exhale. This would mean that if you inhale for 7 seconds, hold for 28 and exhale for 14. He advises 10 times a day morning, noon and night.

Top Tips

- Start out by being more conscious of your breath when you are short of breath and/or during exercise. If you practise yoga, breathing is incorporated into the movements and is also part of weight lifting. When you go for your walk, focus on your breath and notice when you start needing more oxygen and consciously breathe deeper.

- When a strong emotion comes over you such as anger, anxiety or sorrow take a big deep breath before you respond. Often a situation will require you to control your emotions and taking a few deep breaths will help you do so.
- Prior to an event that you are nervous about, such as a presentation at work or job interview, take 10 minutes to practise some deep breathing prior.
- If you have a desk job, which can generate poor posture, take a moment at your desk to put your shoulders back, chin up, sit tall and take a few deep breaths. Or even practise good posture as you are walking down the street, you will find that correcting your posture will allow you to breathe deeper.
- Develop a daily ritual of deep breathing exercises. You don't have to follow Anthony Robbins' recommendation, do some research and find out what works for you.
- Be adventurous and try a yoga, Pilates or Thai Chi class where breath is part of the practise.

So next time you feel yourself getting anxious when you miss the bus or your train is cancelled or the myriad of other frustrations that are just a part of life take a deep breath and chill! We get ourselves worked up over such little things in our day that honestly won't matter next month or next year; taking a few deep breaths is the fastest way to calm down and stay in control of your emotions and your day!

"Deep breaths are like little love notes for your body"

—Anon.

Skin

I have been paranoid about growing older since my late twenties. No different than most women but being so depressed and unhappy with life seemed to increase that fear. The perceived aging reflection in the mirror was just another reminder that I hadn't achieved in life what I believed I should have by 30, 35, 40. *How am I going to find a man if I am old?* Repeating those thoughts now makes me cringe. But was I alone in feeling this way?

I was therefore beyond paranoid about my skin, and watching wrinkles appear as the years went by caused endless stress. I also had the issue of my sun addiction and the growing pigmentation that I could see on my face and arms in particular.

I grew up in the age of worshiping the sun, with no sunscreen but baby oil for a quicker, deeper tan. I really didn't have the right skin type for this constant sun exposure, and going to the beach on the weekend was so ingrained in me I just couldn't relax if the sun was out and I wasn't in it. My vanity overrode any common sense, and I had to have that healthy, natural tan look. I am not alone again, am I?

I broke my sun addiction at 38. My mother had managed to give up the sun at around the same age; however, she suffered from continual recurring surface skin cancers that needed to be burnt off every winter. I watched this for years and didn't take the initiative to wear sunscreen. When I did finally make the break from the beach lifestyle and my tan-less, damaged skin started to emerge, I was horrified!

So began my endless pursuit of laser procedures, expensive creams and injections to remove the sun damage and wrinkles. My mother was no different; I will never forget seeing her after a serious chemical peel. She looked like she had been torched in a fire! She also took it a step further and had a facelift that I presumed I would do one day also.

Is there no end to what we will do for the sake of vanity? As women, we are constantly trying to fight the aging process and reclaim our youthful skin. Is it any wonder when we see air brushed celebrities in the media?

What is Skin?

Skin is the largest organ—yes, it is an organ of your body despite being on the outside. It provides our vital internal organs with protection and holds us all in place, so to speak. It is what we use to touch and is how we feel the outside world. Skin also brings us the opportunity to hate and criticise ourselves for wrinkles, sun spots, stretch marks, cellulite, fat, scars, pimples, spots and pigmentation.

Food and Skin

Glowing healthy, youthful, clear, wrinkle-free skin is not going to come from abusing your body with alcohol, drugs and junk food. It doesn't matter how clever the marketing is on that expensive cream you have been sucked into buying. If you are not giving your body the right fuel and loads of water, you are wasting your money; it's that simple. If you want to wind back the clock on your skin, you have to look at what you are putting into, not onto, your body.

The beauty industry has cleverly got us all to believe that face cream, facials and treatments are the reason the stars that promote them have flawless (air brushed) skin. Marketing and the media has got us all believing that what we see in the mirror is not good enough. The beauty industry is not about helping us feel beautiful at all; it is about ensuring that we feel inadequate enough to buy their products! I am sure I am not alone at feeling like hiding my face when I walk into the cosmetic area of any department store. The lights are bright to show up your every flaw on purpose! Unless you work on TV, who lives their life under spotlights every day?

The beauty industry is all about making you feel embarrassed and ashamed of your natural features. Then the media come along and ensure you see an endless parade of women with flawless skin and loads of makeup. Don't forget that sexual attraction, feeling beautiful about yourself, falling in love and having sex—all pre-date modern cosmetics; otherwise, we wouldn't be here! The aim of the beauty industry is to ensure you feel insecure so you have to buy their cream to correct your perceived flaws.

My skin has been getting younger and younger ever since I started my bodybuilding journey, despite my years of tanning. I have watched wrinkles disappear! I look at myself in the mirror at the gym, and I can't believe how my skin literally glows!

Top Tips

- Drink more than two litres of filtered water every day.
- Eat clean as described in previous chapters.
- Use organic, unscented soap and cream with no parabens, chemicals or toxins.
- Take supplements to enhance skin quality. This includes fish oil, coconut oil, apple cider vinegar, COQ10, biotin.
- Get eight to nine hours of sleep every night.
- Dry brush every morning before you shower.
- Cleanse and tone with organic products and then rose hip oil at night.

I no longer have botox—after having it every three months without fail for many, many years. And while my new routine has improved my skin tremendously, I do think it is more about what has improved on the inside of me. Being comfortable with your aging skin is far more about being comfortable with who you are and where you are at in life. Once you arrive at a place of peace with yourself, you and your skin take on a beauty all your own that makes you truly beautiful. You see it's not about what is on the outside that makes you beautiful; it is the energy you radiate. If you don't feel good about yourself, it doesn't matter what is on the outside. We have all met or seen stunning-looking men and women who are truly ugly people once they open their mouth!

"The skin is a true symbol of our health because it's the last place to get nutrition and if you can drive all of those nutrients all the way to the skin then you know its gotten everywhere else. That's something to recognise."
—Dr David Wolfe
Food Matters, FMTV

Body Love

For the purposes of this chapter and at the end of the body section I am talking about the love of the physical body. The actual form that our body takes on—the body that houses our soul and the feelings we have about our own body. Does that make you feel uncomfortable..?

I saw my body purely as the source to my self-worth. Although I could never articulate my issues in this way, I just knew that I had to keep my figure and my looks, otherwise I seriously didn't know who I was. The thought of getting older and losing it was horrifying to me. I had never been supported or loved unconditionally for the person that I am, so I created a misguided belief that the exterior was all that I had going for me. I was fortunate enough to be slim and relatively attractive—surely that was enough to make me happy and bring success..? Even when I was in my darkest days I can remember people saying to me, "But you are so attractive! You have everything going for you! "Yeah; those sort of comments help... Just because I have the socially acceptable exterior means that life was supposed to be rosy? Being slim, blonde and attractive is the answer...? So I held onto it for dear life!

And as we explored earlier, this is how I started out on my bodybuilding journey. As cardio had been ripped away from me, I had a new avenue to source my dependency on the exterior. And this new avenue just may give me the perfect female form, *and I get to strut around on stage! Then I will seriously have succeeded in finding happiness...* or so I thought.

Pampering and taking care of my body was something I had always done, but once again my motivation was vanity rather than lovingly taking care of my body. This is not something I learned on my journey to stage; the hair, nails, waxing and tanning required for stage was not foreign to me. But there are two different ways to approach these feminine routines. If your mindset is to compete with other women or purely to look good and feed your ego like it was for me, it is not a healthy approach to looking after your body

What is Body Love?

Body love to me encompasses every chapter we have covered so far. Doing everything we can to maintain our health is the ultimate in loving and nourishing our bodies in order to enjoy life and feel the incredible empowerment that comes from owning a body bursting with premium health and vitality. But I want to take it one step further now, particularly if you are struggling with self-worth that has been tied to your body as too many of us women do. I am not alone here, and I hope my story shows that even if you have the body, it is not the answer to finding happiness.

Some interesting statistics:

- Eighty percent of women hate their bodies (that keep them alive).
- Seven out of ten women have an "I hate my body moment" every day.
- Eighty-two percent of women hate their midsection (that digests food to keep them alive).
- Forty-seven percent hate their legs (that take them wherever they want to go).
- Thirty-nine percent hate their arms (that enable them to carry things) and butt (that enables them to sit and walk).
- Thirty-seven percent hate their skin (that holds them together).

Pause for a moment and think about life in a wheelchair without your legs or how you would handle life without any arms. Would you rather have perfect legs or no legs at all?

Loving and appreciating your body is really, really hard. Believe it or not, even being slim I have hated my skin, butt, knees, nose, thighs and breasts. (Yes, I have had breast augmentation for anyone who is wondering) So even though this chapter might make you feel uncomfortable, please have an open mind. You might not be ready to try this one until you have incorporated all the previous chapters into your life and are beginning to lose weight.

Pampering and grooming your body is not for everyone, but we all have some form of feminine routine to conform with what society expects a woman to look like. When you are trying to build self-confidence and feel good about yourself, I believe it is important to love and really appreciate every aspect of your physical being and that means taking care of and loving all the parts of your body that you hate! Too often when we don't feel good about ourselves, we will let some of our feminine maintenance slip or just do the bare minimum—because no one sees but me.. Most of us have heard the joke about how fast women can shave their legs when sex is imminent! We shouldn't do these things just for our partner! But for ourselves.

We all have different maintenance either daily, weekly, monthly or quarterly to present ourselves in a feminine way according to our own personal style. When we don't feel good about ourselves, it is even more important to make the effort. I have a rule that I am always ready for sex! That doesn't mean I am necessarily going to get lucky, but I feel that if I can do that stuff for a man, I can do it for myself! Besides, you never know when you might be in an accident and wind up in hospital with a cute doctor. ☺

But, seriously, we often approach these body rituals with the mindset of *I have to do it to look the part, to look good, to compete with others, to not embarrass myself.* Do we really enjoy actually doing it when we are hating our bodies, trying to hide this or that? Then we stand back once we're all done up with the hair and makeup and criticize ourselves further! How often do you look in the mirror and think, *damn I am hot! I look fantastic!* Why not?

So what does your maintenance list look like? Waxing, shaving, moisturizing, washing hair, applying makeup and perfume? And what sort of things do you do to treat yourself ? It is a good idea to reward yourself with a facial or massage rather than with food! Whatever your maintenance is it is important to stick with it and start approaching it with love and incorporate treats to go that little bit further to make you feel special.

Top Tips

- Schedule it. Whatever your maintenance list looks like, make sure it is scheduled into your busy life. Do you wash your hair or shave your legs every Sunday afternoon? Do you go to the beautician? Whether it be for regular waxing/laser or a facial treat, make sure these appointments are in your diary. They are important!
- Be mindful. As you are shaving, waxing, moisturising or washing your hair, do it mindfully. Lovingly caress and massage your skin as you would your baby or lover. (yes really!) rather than just go through the motions, really look, feel and appreciate your skin that holds your body together, your eyes as you put on makeup for allowing you to see. What is your best physical feature? Notice it and be appreciative. And don't notice the things you don't like!
- Dry brushing. To assist with detoxing your body, support weight loss, improve circulation, help reduce cellulite, build immunity and increase cell renewal, incorporate dry brushing before your shower every day. The health benefits are enormous and it gives you the opportunity to stroke, appreciate and love your skin, legs, thighs, butt and arms! Follow up with moisturiser after the shower, remembering to lovingly caress.

- Look at yourself naked in the mirror while dry brushing and moisturising. Yes, I did just write that. And yes, I know it can be really, really hard! I have gone through stages of avoiding the bathroom mirror. But aren't you avoiding yourself? How can you get to the point of loving your body and feeling good about yourself if you won't even look at you? So take a peek and start appreciating how lucky you are just to have the eyes to see! Start with just looking at the part that you like. Great breasts? So look at them and appreciate what you see. Skip over the parts you don't like for now, but once you adopt all the previous chapters, I promise you there will be more parts you like.
- Tongue brushing. Assists with toxin removal, improves your breath and digestive health, and will give you that clean feeling so you can taste your food better. And be ready for that passionate kiss! First thing in the morning after your digestive system has been resting overnight, take off the film that has accumulated on your tongue before or after you brush your teeth. Yuk! Who wants that in your stomach? As you are doing it, appreciate your tongue as it allows you to taste yummy food!
- Detox bath. Time often prevents us from having a relaxing bath, so make it a once a week ritual to soak in epsom salts (extra magnesium bonus), baking soda and bit of lavender oil. This will again assist your body detoxify, but it will also soothe your muscles and give you some "me" time to relax. There are no bubbles in this bath, so you can also take a peek at your body again. You could even do some deep breathing or try to meditate as there is nothing more visual than watching your breath while the water rocks with

each inhale and exhale. Lock the bathroom door for half an hour and take some time out!

- Treat yourself. To a manicure, pedicure, massage, facial or whatever a treat means to you. When I get my nails done, I just sit there in sheer joy. Such luxury! To have a couple of girls tending to my feet and hands. Bliss! Having beautiful nails is a sure fire way to lift my mood!
- Buy some sexy lingerie. Yes, you read that right! You don't have to tell anyone if you don't want to. You don't have to spend a lot of money either. Maybe you have some already buried at the bottom of your drawer. Wear it to work or as you are running around after the kids or just doing your daily, mundane, nonsexy routine. Try it once a week. You will forget you are wearing it as you lose yourself in your day. But when you go to the bathroom you will remember. How do you feel?!
- Keep it up. How are the soles of your feet looking? After you have had a pedicure, invest in a pumice stone and keep up the scrubbing so your feet are silky smooth. Is your nail polish chipped? Take it all off until you can have a manicure or paint your nails yourself. How often do you get colour done in your hair? If you colour your hair, make sure you have regular appointments to touch up your roots. Getting your hair done is another sure fire way to lift your mood!

In order to feel good in your own body, you need to treat yourself as you would someone you love. Your body is a miraculous machine that takes loving care of you and keeps you alive every day; even when you don't love your body it keeps on loving you! So you should treat it accordingly, in a way that enhances your sense of self and well-being. Be proud of this physical being that houses your soul, and stop the endless stream of self-criticism chatter that we women seem to constantly obsess about. Our bodies are not who we are, but how we treat our bodies is a true reflection of how we feel about ourselves. What is your body telling the world of how you feel about you?

To feel sexy, confident and good about ourselves and in order to share our body with our partner, we need to love and tend to our physical aspects. If you don't feel passionate and good about your body how can you expect your partner to? It is not self-indulgent, and there is nothing wrong with having pride in your appearance. I believe it is of the utmost importance!

*"Did you ever realise how much your body loves you? It's always trying to keep you alive. It's making sure you breathe while you sleep, stopping cuts from bleeding, fixing broken bones, finding ways to beat the illnesses you might catch. Your body literally loves you so much....
It's time to start loving it back!"*

—Anon.

Body Conclusion

So am I too over the top and obsessed to not only do all these things but to commit a large chunk of my income to my body and health? Many will say that I am wasting my money. But I look at it very differently. To me, this is an investment in myself and my future health and quality of life. It is my insurance policy. It is also the reason for my recovery from a life of sheer misery, so why wouldn't I be obsessed with it? I was wasting away the same amount of money on therapy and partying! I am looking, feeling and acting years younger than my biological age, and I can guarantee you that when I am 80, I will still be lifting weights and looking more like 60. I can also guarantee you that my health care costs will be less than half of the majority of the population in my retirement. Have you factored in additional retirement savings to cover your health?

If you have aging parents or have seen what happens in nursing homes, then maybe it is worth considering your health now while you are young enough to preserve it and prevent this happening to you. It is not a given that we suffer in our senior years. It is now a choice, and the information is out there if you choose to educate yourself. We don't have to suffer as we get older, and I certainly don't want to rely on anyone in my old age to wipe my bum! I want quality of life and to do everything I want to do up until the day I die. Why do too many of us sacrifice long-term health strategies for short-term satisfaction or entertainment? What use are those designer shoes or handbag when you are struggling with a walking frame (walker)?

The other factor most people think about is time. I hear all the time that I don't have the time! To exercise, to cook, to get more sleep. In this technological age, everything in life has become so fast and our expectation is to get things immediately! Which has included food. I freely admit that my lifestyle is selfish, and my life is dedicated to my health 24/7. My health is my priority in life, so I would encourage you to examine your own priorities. Is watching TV and time on social media more important than your health? I realize with children there is less time for yourself, but isn't teaching children the importance of taking care of their own health important? I know plenty of mothers who compete, and there is even a bodybuilding division just for mothers. I have the utmost respect for these incredible women who live my lifestyle and compete! The time is there; it is all a matter of priorities.

When I was growing up, we all sunbaked in baby oil. We didn't know better, and we were not educated otherwise. When my parents were growing up, everyone smoked. They didn't know better, and they were not educated otherwise. We live in an age where we eat everything that is on the supermarket shelves and believe that someone else is responsible for looking out for what enters our one model-issued, has-to-last-a-lifetime body. Isn't this the same as sunbaking and smoking? But the difference now is we don't have to research in a library or rely on the media (which is often incorrect) to supply us with the information. The Internet has opened up the most amazing educational tool in the history of mankind, and yet we too often don't use it to educate ourselves!

More and more evidence is coming to light that our modern, fast-food diet is just as fatal as sunbaking and smoking. The movement is slowly building, and with documentaries like Food Matters and Hungry for Change, as well as many others, awareness is growing. It may take decades yet, but the tide is slowly turning. I am beyond passionate about making my contribution, and I hope that

I have motivated you to do further research and incorporate some of these things into your health routine.

> *"If you think the pursuit of good health is expensive and time consuming. Try illness."*
> —Lee Swanson
> *Food Matters, FMTV*

AGELESS MIND

"*I believe that health is more than merely the absence of disease. It is a total state of physical, mental, emotional, spiritual and social wellbeing.*"

—Dr Frank Lipman
Food Matters, FMTV

Finding Myself from the Outside In

Ageless Mind

Most people would say that you must have a strong mind to compete in the bodybuilding world. I definitely agree! Most would say you need to start out with this strong mind to go through the gruelling training and strict diet, but I am not sure that many actually do as quite clearly we bodybuilders are heavily into achieving this image of the perfect body. So vanity can play a part in the motivation, which may have underlining self-esteem issues and, in extreme cases, narcissistic elements. Some may start the bodybuilding journey and not overcome these personal issues. I am not sure I would have if I hadn't made the decision to compete.

I soon realised that I had completely overcommitted myself as far as getting up on stage. The hardest part for me to date was the diet and change in lifestyle; the training was the easy part, despite the physical pain I endured. But both these elements pale into insignificance when I thought about strutting around in a bikini on stage. I was having nightmares about it! Arnold Schwarzenegger always said that to be successful on stage you should incorporate the posing into your training sessions at the gym. That is how important it is to your success in the bodybuilding world! If you don't nail the stage presence, then all your hard work in the gym and kitchen is wasted. The judges are not just assessing your body condition but how you carry yourself, how confidently you move, how you hold the required poses to show off your hard work. I knew all of this, so how was I going to do it sober?!!

And so, once again, fuelled by vanity and, yet to come into my awareness, low self-esteem, I had to find a way to get this broken girl on stage. I knew I had to work on my confidence, I knew I had to work on my mind and, once again, fool the world, as I had always done, about how shy and broken I actually was. I have tried to hide the real me my entire life, and here I was going to this huge extreme. What on earth was I thinking?! So I hired a fitness model and a catwalk model to help me learn how to walk and pose on stage. I really wasn't very good, and while I practised and practised without the inner confidence and belief, of course it was going to show!

The other influence for me with addressing my mind and confidence issues was the support I had around me. Like any athlete, you need a range of different professionals to support you on a physical level, but if you are lucky like I was, these same people mentor you on a mental and spiritual level as well. While I did not have much support through my personal network, I had paid support that was different from anything I had experienced before. I was not used to being motivated and mentored in this way. I was not used to being treated with respect! And despite the fact I was paying them, I could see the passion, enthusiasm and personal reward they gained from helping me succeed. Their support of me was far more than just a job to them. Maybe helping others to succeed was something I should look into..

And so my spiritual journey begins. The second half of the book is all about habits that I undertook to get myself on stage, as well as a few lessons learned since, which inadvertently assisted me in stumbling across the answers I had been looking for my entire life. Having had no self-awareness for 46 years, with my deep-seated emotional issues driving me towards stage and with six weeks off work prior to my first competition, I had the time and space to work on my mind. Having started down this road for all the wrong reasons, I now continue to learn, grow and become more aware every day. These habits have not only changed my entire outlook on life, but I now finally have a healthy relationship with myself. I finally found self-respect from the outside in.

"The quickest way to acquire self-confidence is to do exactly what you are afraid to do."

—Anon.

Finding Myself from the Outside In

Therapy v Mentoring

The Background on my Brokenness

I have been in and out of therapy since the age of 16, born from a difficult childhood with my parents splitting at an early age and associated mismanagement of the impact this has on the children. Not a unique story by any means. My adult years were littered with broken relationships, broken marriages, and my heart has been broken more times than I care to remember. Without the foundation of an ideal parental marriage to serve as a role model, I had no clue what a healthy relationship looked like. Coupled with my own lack of self-worth, depression was my constant companion for most of my adult life.

I even checked myself into a clinic for depression once, only to realise that I really didn't belong there, and on my attempts to discharge myself, I was then shipped off—in an ambulance, mind you, under court order—to a public psychiatric ward where I was drugged to my eyeballs and could not get out without parental consent. (I was 39...) I have made two attempts on my life; the first was just a cry for help, the second a more serious one. I have been addicted to alcohol, marijuana and various painkillers. For a long period of time I was drunk or stoned every night of the week. I have wanted to die more times than I can remember. I spent my 30s and 40s on various anti-depressants, some the serious SSRI (selective serotonin reuptake inhibitor) kind (like Prozac). I spent three days watching my mother die from a fall. She worked the day she died, and she was not in poor health, other than early stages of dementia. It wasn't until three months after this sudden, tragic event that her death was investigated for potential homicide.

So if you are wondering where my opinion comes from on this topic of therapy, sadly, it comes from firsthand experience over many, many years!

We are a product of modern medicine. We have been brought up to believe that doctors are gods, and whatever they say or recommend is the only solution to our illness or problems. In matters of the mind, of which no general practitioner has training in, we are referred to psychiatrists. For a long time, the government endorsed this by allowing us to claim subsidised fees through the Medicare system. What's worse is that psychiatrists are trained in administrating psychiatric drugs, and most of these doctors are actually paid commission on these drugs! I have read numerous stories, which never seem to make it to mainstream media, of people being prescribed so many different drugs they completely lose themselves and their life. I witnessed this first hand with my little stint in a public psychiatric ward. On admission I was stripped of all my personal belongings, I had no way to contact the outside world, and I was left in a room and dosed up on who knows what. I have only vague memories of coming in and out of drug induced haze. Both my brother and ex-husband tried to have me released to no avail. My father had to fly up from Melbourne to secure my release! What could have happened to me? I was one of the fortunate ones and only lost three days of my life.

Recently the government has extended its subsidised funding to psychologists. But only for a certain amount of sessions—you are supposed to be "fixed" after 10 sessions? So from the age of 16 I have seen dozens and dozens of psychiatrists, psychologists, therapists, psychoanalysts and counsellors using the traditional therapy approach. Sessions are usually spent talking, analysing and dissecting events of the past to establish why we are still suffering. Whether it be events from childhood or the events of last week. While there is some value in being aware of the events that shape us, I am not sure that reliving the past over and over is a healthy way to approach the future. The past is just a story you keep telling yourself in your mind. It is not real, you can't get in your car and drive there, so why keep telling yourself a story that hurts? It is important to forgive and be at peace with your past, sure, but every session I would walk out in tears and feeling worse! Was this negative energy propelling me towards a happier life?

Traditional therapy certainly can be useful in some circumstances. For some, this may be enough. For, some traditional therapy will work just fine. But for me, after 20 odd years of going over the same ground, with two attempts on my life, constant addictions and three hospital visits, was it really working?

Mentor Therapy

I did deviate slightly from the traditional approach around my mid-thirties. I was fortunate enough that a trusted friend referred me to a naturopath. Not just your everyday naturopath but one specialising in sports nutrition for athletes. Back then I was not the athlete I am today, but I was a gym junkie, so I was very open to pursuing this opportunity and I really admired and respected this women. Plus she did more than just look at my diet; she actually gave me practical suggestions for a better way to live. I tried kinesiology through this period also. Finally my eyes were being opened to the alternate way, but, unfortunately, I was not done with my self-destruction just yet. But it did lay a foundation. I often look back and see that it was my first step in the right direction. And it did bring awareness to this alternate way of trying to "fix" myself.

A few more years of misery, a new therapist or two, and a change in medication went by before I happened to be recommended to an energetic healer. Wow! Now I was really going against the traditional method! Each session I felt so loved and supported. Each session I would go home feeling great, even if I did have a big cry! Each session was about healing the past and moving beyond the pain. I really didn't understand the method, but I believed and, once again, respected and admired the practitioner.

During my journey to stage the first time I engaged with a hypnotherapist. I was in a fairly depressed and negative state for most of my comp prep, and I knew I needed help to overcome this. With my history of alternate therapists, I had not tried hypnotherapy before and felt I needed to be hypnotised, preferably while I was actually on stage!

I have also seen a transformational healer more recently who incorporates reiki, kinesiology, vibrational healing and clearing emotional blockages held in the body. A truly amazing women! And a turning point in my recovery.

All these women provided me with mentoring that I had never had before. They all either had qualities that I wanted to have, or they had overcome similar issues to mine. I looked up to and admired them; I don't ever remember feeling this way about my therapists. How can you really help and support someone through an emotional crisis by simply reading and memorising a text book at university?

Get Yourself a Coach!

Having a mentor or coach is a relatively new concept; however, you will not find many successful entrepreneurs or athletes who don't have a number of professionals supporting them and moving them towards their goals. Athletes have always had them, but we are now beginning to recognise the value this can bring to any goal in life.

I always associated mentors and coaches with successful people. I didn't think that a broken person like me would fit the ideal client profile, so I didn't seek out this type of professional to help me, and, of course, doctors send you to traditional therapy anyway. With my decision to compete and become a fitness model, I naturally sought out experts to assist me to achieve this goal. As I was not seeking this help to "fix" me, I felt comfortable engaging with these professionals. Although I did have to be careful to hide the broken side of me!

The universe was certainly looking after me when I landed a personal trainer who became my mentor and coach on a spiritual level also. Not only did he train my body to compete, he has also mentored me in many other aspects of my life and has been a pivotal part of my journey and recovery.

It doesn't matter what you want to achieve in life; there is someone out there who has either already achieved it or can mentor and support you to achieve it. Far more positive and productive than traditional therapy, don't you think? While there are generalised "life" coaches out there, I am not a fan. You see, it is very difficult to achieve anything in life, including overcoming depression or just finding happiness without achieving physical health. Premium health will lead to success and happiness every single time!

Top Tips

- Set your goal. I know this can be a tough one when all you feel is unhappy with life. What is missing in your life? Where do you want to be in a year's time? Where do you want to be in five years' time? What are you passionate about? Is it career, relationship or health related?
- Seek out the right professional. There are many different types of coaches out there these days. A life coach is the most common and is good for career and relationship goals; however, as I am biased, I don't believe you can achieve anything in life without your body performing in peak condition. A health coach is a relatively new profession that combines your well-being in its entirety. If you have a more specific goal related to fitness, then choose a personal trainer or yoga instructor. If you are just looking at

physical goals, however, make sure you dig a bit deeper. Is losing weight tied to your self-worth? Executive coaches specialise in career focused goals. Most entrepreneurs will have different coaches and mentors along their journey to success; from start-up, to launching, to social media, to building a client base, there is a business coach out there who can support and guide you.

- Do your homework. If I am going to move forward towards my goals, I need to admire, respect and look up to anyone who is supporting me—this is non-negotiable. Like any relationship in your life, just as you are selective with your friends and partner, you should be just as choosy with the people you are going to pay money to support you. Not just whoever your doctor sends you to! Thoroughly read their websites and like their social media pages. Do their posts and philosophy attract you? Read their testimonials. Read their bios. Can you relate? You are looking for respect, integrity and professionalism. Above all, do they inspire you?

- Invest in yourself. If you want to fast-track change and engage support to do so, there is no getting around the fact that it will cost money. I spent a fortune on my journey to stage, but I also spent a fortune the previous 30 odd years on traditional therapy that got me nowhere. Which fortune would you rather spend? I resent the traditional therapy cost, but I don't for one second regret the cost I have paid to finally find myself. I prefer to spend at least three months with my clients, which doesn't seem like much if you have been battling for so many years already.

- Commit. This is your future we are talking about; this is your life! Life is not meant to be lived in mediocrity or unhappiness. I promise the sacrifices you make now will be worth it tenfold when you realise your dreams and get to a place of empowerment, peace and happiness.

"We become like the five people we spend the most time with. Surround yourself with those that influence you with positivity, encouragement and contribute to your well-being and success."

—Anon.

Monkey Mind

I don't think I was that different from the majority on this topic; *what is this meditation rubbish?* Sitting in silence with just me was waaaaaay too confronting. When I spent all my time trying to escape the thoughts in my head, why would I want to go through the agony, even if it was for only 10 minutes?

I had been told through my alternate therapists that I needed to meditate, and I had read this advice in many books. This was the way to calm my mind and get control of my emotions, they said. But I wasn't listening and continued to resist; it was just too hard and painful. I would much rather block out my thoughts with drugs or alcohol or TV or keeping busy or any distraction at all to take me out of myself.

And, really, that monkey mind inside my head was uncontrollable, wasn't it? I couldn't even begin to imagine how I could stop it; in fact, I didn't even think it was possible. Wasn't my monkey mind me?

Over the years I had made attempts to try meditation—never sitting in silence, though. I bought a few guided meditation CDs that I would drag out when I was in a really bad place only to put them back after a couple of goes. I had one CD that my energetic healer gave me that she always played during our sessions; the process with an energetic healer is through meditation, so listening to this CD took me back to the loving place I felt when I was with her. But without her guiding me, I gave up.

I even tried a few meditation day courses and drop-in classes run by local Buddhists; they were always so happy and calm. I could see that I wanted a piece of their peace! I knew what it was all about, knew how to do it, but didn't see the benefit so I never stuck with a regular practise..

What is Meditation?

Meditation is critical to your emotional well-being; many of us have heard that somewhere. But isn't it only for Buddhist monks? You will find that most successful people in the world will have some form of meditation practise, and you will be amazed at the benefits it provides once you make it a regular habit. It will reduce your stress levels, provide emotional stability, lower blood pressure, bring calmness to your mind, allow you to handle difficult situations with greater ease and confidence, develop your intuition and give you more clarity of thought. It will even result in more creativity in your life. Sounds too good to be true, doesn't it?! Isn't it easier just to take a pill or have a drink?!

Traditional meditation is sitting with your back straight and both feet on the floor, somewhere you won't be disturbed. You can either close your eyes or focus—that single focus stare when you are aware of your peripheral vision but your eyes glaze over—on a particular object if you prefer. A candle is often used. Take a couple of big deep breaths. Scan your body and relax every part, one by one. Go back to normal breathing and focus on your breath; count if you like, but really listen to your breath as it goes in and out. What does the air feel like going in and out of your nostrils? Can you feel your chest rising and falling? What does the texture of your clothing feel like on your skin? What is the air temperature, and what does it feel like? What sounds can you hear both outside the room and inside? Maybe a bird chirping or a clock ticking. If thoughts come into your mind from the past or future, just notice them but don't entertain the thought. Bring your awareness back to your breath and be present in the moment. Sound easy?

So why do we want to be in the present moment? I am sure you have heard this before, too—because that is where you will find peace! Yeah, I didn't believe it either, for a very long time. How could it possibly be that simple?! But when you realise the past is now just a story you keep telling yourself in your mind and you certainly can't change it, you recognize what a waste of your precious time it is to worry or think about it. And the future is yet to happen, so there is little point in worrying or stressing over it either. There is a big difference between planning and excessively overthinking about what is ahead. The present moment is the only point in time that you actually have any control over, and with regular meditation practise you will find that you are enjoying the here and now more and, therefore, becoming happier and more content. Really?! There are a few more techniques to add to meditation to enjoy the present moment but, yes, it is possible!

So Back to Getting on Stage

I was stressing big time about this. Like I mentioned in the last chapter, I started seeing a hypnotist to help me get on stage, I knew I had to work on my mind. I was practising the walk and poses, and I knew I could learn the steps, but it was my attitude I had to work on! I had to own that stage, and I had to show the judges that I loved being up there—which is the last thing I felt!

Hypnotism is all about taking you to a place in your mind to reduce peripheral awareness and enhance the capacity of response to suggestions. It is attempting to change underlying beliefs or habits. But the process to get you into a hypnotic state is just meditation. So I would have my sessions with my hypnotist and I also started listening to hypnotic CDs every night before bed to work on my self-confidence. I was pretty broken hearted during this time, so it wasn't just about getting up on stage but also trying to, once again, put another relationship behind me.

So here I was forcing myself into a situation where I had to pick up a regular practise of meditation for the sake of strutting around in a bikini. I not only did my nightly practise, I also incorporated a few things into my day to try and stop the depressing thoughts of the past and also my rising panic of getting up on stage. I installed a couple of apps on my phone that supported me in staying in the present moment all day as well as using any idle time on the bus to do the same.

Inadvertently I was learning to live in the present moment. Inadvertently I was learning to quieten my mind and take control of my emotions. Inadvertently I was learning skills that were going to serve me well past my competition. And I didn't even know it!

Top Tips

- Get up 20 minutes earlier. When the house is quiet and you can enjoy some silence. Starting your day with a meditation is a sure-fire way to have an awesome day!
- Make it part of your wind down for sleep routine. Doing 10 minutes of meditation before bed is a perfect way to leave the stresses of the day behind you so you can sleep peacefully. It will definitely support you in sleeping better.
- Exercise. My main meditation is my gym time. Nothing like focusing on physical movements to bring you into the present moment. From walking to yoga to cardio to Pilates to weight training. Whatever you enjoy, focus on your miraculous body moving.
- Do what you love. Ever noticed how when you are doing something that you absolutely love that time stands still? Isn't that bringing you into the present moment? More on this in a later chapter.
- Get into nature. When you go for a walk in the bush, what do you see, smell, hear? Nature has almost foreign aspects that we have forgotten about living in cities like we do. Tune into

Mother Nature, and she is guaranteed to bring you into the present moment and relieve stress!

- Don't just wait, meditate! When you are waiting for an appointment, friend, meeting or whatever, instead of reaching for your phone to text or check Facebook, download a mediation app and tune out for 5 minutes into peace and calm!

- Dishes. Or any other mundane household chore. Next time you mindlessly do one of your daily chores, such as brushing your teeth or showering, things you have done a million times and on autopilot, deliberately notice every little detail. For example, when doing dishes, feel the temperature of the water on your hands. What does the detergent smell like? What sounds are the dishes making as you wash and put them on the rack? How many bubbles can you see in the sink? Use all your senses and really be present with what you are doing.

- Drive time. Ever get to your destination and not remember how you got there? Your monkey mind completely took over, and you were on autopilot. So instead (and to be safer!), be present to everything you see on the road. Notice the names of the street signs, the person walking down the street, the sound of the engine and gear changes, the smell of your car and try driving in silence for a change!

- Drop in Classes. Most cities will have a local Buddhist group that run meditation classes that only require a small donation to participate. Or try your local community college or wellness centre. Educate yourself on the different types of meditation and find out what works best for you.

The opportunities to meditate throughout the day are endless and don't have to be the traditional method. The more you can stay present with everything you are doing the happier and more peaceful your life will become. I didn't believe this either, but, trust me, it works!

"Meditation and visualisation can change you from the inside out. I don't know of more powerful tools for transforming your body and your life."
—Jon Gabriel
Food Matters, FMTV

Affirmations

Similar to meditation, I dismissed affirmations as a load of hooey. How ridiculous repeating words that are just nonsense—and looking in the mirror while doing it? Are you crazy?! The most common use of affirmations is to improve self-confidence; I knew this. I couldn't say I love myself to myself! And, anyway, I already do love myself. Yeah, clearly all my self-destructive behaviour, addictions and attempts on my life were due to my bulletproof self-esteem! I really didn't understand all this fuss about having to love yourself, I didn't feel it applied to me, and I certainly wasn't going to start saying it out loud.

I had read about the importance of affirmations to change your beliefs and mindset, and once again my alternate healers had recommended it. Healers often have you repeat affirmations during a session, but it feels very different repeating words back to someone in comparison to initiating it yourself. I even bought a Louise Hay affirmation CD and listened to it once. I also bought a beautiful deck of Louise Hay "I can do it" affirmation cards that lived in my bottom drawer. Once again I wasn't ready to receive the lesson.

What are Affirmations?

An affirmation is a positive sentence or phrase aimed to affect the conscious and the subconscious mind. When you say them, think them or hear them, they can become the thoughts that create your reality. It is a way to consciously control your thoughts, generate associated feelings about these statements and another way to bring you into the present moment.

Research tells us we have between 45,000 to 51,000 thoughts a day and well over the majority of these thoughts are negative. If you are not aware of your thoughts and allow that monkey mind to take over, then without even realising it you are negatively impacting your thoughts, beliefs and therefore your life. When you start to consciously choose positive thoughts through affirmations, when you declare confidently and assertively that the statement is true, you can literally re-program your mind!

Where Do We Learn Self-confidence aka Self-love?

Learning to love ourselves and honour ourselves with self-respect is yet another critical skill that is not taught in schools. And yet it is vital to leading a happy and successful life. Why is this?

So our poor parents are left with this critical lesson. And if they struggle with their own internal demons and don't possess this invaluable trait, then how do they pass it on to their children? Can our parents even articulate this is a lesson that needs to be taught? Children learn far more by copying behaviour and attitude than verbal lessons and discipline. I know my parents were from the generation that didn't talk about feelings and loving yourself was a derogatory term; you were said to be "up yourself." Fostering good feelings about yourself was certainly not part of my childhood. Put that together with all the childhood traumas I endured and my parents' own self-esteem issues, is it any wonder that I grew up hating myself?!

Back to Stage, Stripper Heels and Bikinis

So here I was doing my meditations, and I remembered my Louise Hay affirmation cards. I dragged them out from the bottom drawer and started sifting through. I was now very aware that I needed to work on my confidence (all for the sake of stage) and maybe some of those affirmations might help also.

"I love me! Just the way I am... unconditionally!"

"I am comfortable looking at myself in the mirror and saying 'I love you!'"
"I deeply love and approve of myself. I am a perfect reflection of my beautiful soul. I love me!"

I had committed to getting up on stage, and I was desperate to achieve my goal, so I stuck all these affirmations around my mirror in the bathroom, and whenever I went to the loo or was brushing my teeth or doing my hair, I started reciting them. Yes, I felt silly, and at times it would bring up negative emotions in me. But bringing those negative emotions into my awareness meant that I could confront and deal with them more easily. My monkey mind would also find reasons why a particular affirmation wasn't true, and I had a lot of trouble looking at myself while saying them. But I persisted and eventually I got to a place where I could say them in a more confident tone, looking myself in the eye.

I then dragged out the dusty Louise Hay affirmation CD, and as my catwalk model lived about an hour's drive away, I would use this time in my car to listen and repeat these affirmations. Very monotonous... but so is the ongoing self-hatred talk!

Dr Joseph Murphy also recommends reciting affirmations as you drift off to sleep. The most powerful time to access your subconscious mind. So every night I would say to myself "I am sexy, confident and I love being on stage!"

Once again I was inadvertently altering the course of my life; inadvertently I was dealing with inner demons that had plagued my entire existence and nearly destroyed my life. Inadvertently I was teaching myself a long overdue lesson all for the sake of getting up on stage in a bikini and stripper heels!

After meditation, affirmations are the next best way to reprogram your mind. It is easy to state things you already believe in like *I love my mum* or *it's a beautiful day today*. But we also need to start saying things that we want to believe and we want (need!) to have as part of our lives. You would be surprised how many negative thoughts are running through your head and imprinting on your subconscious mind. These thoughts create beliefs, and if you are not convinced and truly believe that you can and will achieve your goals, then your subconscious mind will sabotage your efforts.

Top Tips

- Write a list of all your negative qualities. For most of us this is easy! Now write the opposite positive quality that you would like to have. Create a positive I am statement to associate with each positive quality. Now write it on a Post-it note and stick it where you will see it every day—on the bathroom mirror, on your PC or on your fridge. Recite it either out loud or in your head every time you see the affirmation.
- Check out affirmation apps. Have a look at the affirmation apps available. Create your affirmations so they send you a message on your phone at regular intervals. When you see the message, recite either out loud or in your head.
- Recite an affirmation at bedtime. Pick one particular affirmation that is the biggest change you want to make, and recite it over and over in your head after you turn out the light and as your head rests on the pillow prior to sleep.
- Sing! Is there a song that contains an affirmation that resonates with you? I know for me "Uptown Funk" (feat. Bruno Mars) by Mark Ronson was a song I have sang over and over and over and over!
- Download an affirmation program, whether it is subliminal or you can hear the words. Listen to it over and over in the car, on public transport or as you are drifting off to sleep.

- Write down your favourite affirmations every day in your journal. More on this shortly.
- Feel! Make sure you get into the feeling place of each affirmation. To communicate effectively to your subconscious mind, positive feelings are really important! It might take a while to get to this point. Just keep at it.
- Download a program onto your PC that will subliminally flash affirmations at periodic intervals. You can make this as slow or as fast as you like. Slow means you read them on a conscious level, and a fast flash means that your subconscious mind will receive the message without interrupting your work.

"Our thoughts are powerful and what we think and feel is what we create."

—Dr Bradley Nelson
Food Matters, FMTV

Visualisation

J ust like meditation and affirmations... I dismissed using visualisations not just as a load of hooey but as a depressing exercise, as it highlighted how much I hated my life and how far I was from where I wanted to be. As I have mentioned, I was all about avoidance and escape from my misery. I didn't feel I was valuable or worthy. I just thought that the wonderful pictures of a "dream" house/relationship/car/life were not for me. I did not enjoy exposing myself to other people's joy. I was jealous! Life was hard enough for me and it made me feel worse! Depression is very much surviving day to day. It is very hard to see into the future; even making plans for six months' time was hard for me. I lived week to week and only felt any happiness for the future if I had party plans lined up for the coming weekends. So trying to visualise how I wanted my life to be was really, really hard and only upset me further as I just felt I could never achieve it. So, of course, I didn't!

I had touched on vision boards and visualisations in some of the books I had read and even made a half-hearted attempt. When I first watched the movie The Secret, they made it look so easy that if you had a vision board you would achieve. I actually arranged with a girlfriend to make a night of creating our vision boards. But I didn't believe it, I didn't enjoy it and once again, I wasn't ready for the lesson. Like meditation and affirmations I thought this was a waste of time.

But I have to get up on stage...??!!

Serious athletes use visualisations to move them towards their goals. Ask Olympic gold medallists, and they will tell you that prior to winning their gold they played the scene of them winning over and over in their minds prior to the race.

Ask any entrepreneur and they will tell you the same thing; they will have used either visualisations in their mind or through pictures on a vision board that they have meditated on or looked at on a regular basis to achieve their goals.

I was desperate; I had given in to meditation and affirmations, so visualisation was the next piece of the puzzle I had to adopt. I had just read the book *The Power of the Subconscious Mind* by Dr Joseph Murphy. *If I could only access this power that was between my ears!* So every night before I went to sleep, I would play the scene in my mind of me walking on stage and doing the routine I had practised over and over. I had to go there in my mind as frequently as I could so that when I was actually on stage I would feel at home, that I would feel as if I had been there many times before, that I owned the stage and I loved being there! As per my affirmation!

I also tried to train my mind to do this scene over and over at any time of the day though knowing that it was most powerful as I was drifting off to sleep. If I wasn't actually walking back and forth, back and forth, practising my walk and poses, I was pretending in my imagination.

I didn't do a physical vision board at this time, but I did do a virtual one on Pinterest. I love Pinterest, and while I am sceptical on other social media platforms (more on this shortly) I find Pinterest to be awesome for motivation and to translate my hopes and dreams into visual pictures. I highly recommend Pinterest as a positive influence because it is not driven by people's opinions but of beautiful images.

Top Tips

- To make a vision board, invest time clarifying your goals. Decide what part of your life this board will represent and for what period of time. Is this for short-term or long-term goals? You can make several mini-boards for each area with a goal or connect them as one large board. Examples would be relationship, home, work, business or travel.

- After your goals are clear, collect images from magazines, photos or your own sketches. or you can use an online version with Pinterest as I do. I have a profile there, so you can check it out for ideas. Pinterest even has the facility for secret boards; most of my vision boards are here. You could also try PicMonkey to create a virtual board. For "portable" vision boards, use a piece of cardboard to glue or tack images in place or a cork board works well.

- Supplement images with quotes or words that also represent your vision. I am totally obsessed with quotes and spend time reading motivational ones every day on Pinterest. (Check out my Wise Words board!) Pick quotes that resonate with your goals and use vibrant colours to enhance the emotion of these pieces. A vision board represents everything that is you, so creatively express you!

- Display your vision board in a place that is highly visible to you. Popular places to hang vision boards are above computer screens, in offices, next to mirrors, on refrigerators, or any high traffic area of your home or office. You may want to take a photo of your vision board to display on a mobile device. If you are using Pinterest make sure you log in every day; just

before sleep is a good time. You can continually add new photos to your Pinterest vision board to remind yourself of your goals.
- Meditate on these images for a few minutes a day. Visualise these images as part of your life right now. As these visions become reality, acknowledge the success with check marks or stamps recognizing the piece as achieved. give yourself the satisfaction of completion.

Similarly if a vision board doesn't resonate for you, then make sure you play a mind movie of the pictures and scenes you wish to have in your life. Create some affirmations around this scene and make sure you replay it every night as you drift off to sleep. Find the feeling place of actually being in this scene; how does it feel? What can you see around you? What can you smell, touch and hear? What are you wearing? Make it as real as possible and get into the scene and believe with every core of your being that you are there. Yes; once again it feels a bit far-fetched! But every successful athlete and entrepreneur can't be wrong!

"Whatever you hold in your mind on a consistent basis is exactly what you will experience in your life."
—Anthony Robbins
Food Matters, FMTV

Beats

I have always been very in tune with music due to the heavy influence of it in my childhood. My mother was a professional classical violinist and my first stepfather was not only a professional classical violinist also but a conductor. They both were members of a national orchestra, so I grew up either listening to them practise or it playing on the stereo or pupils playing, as Mum taught from home. I played the flute for the majority of my teenage years, and I even played in a youth orchestra that I adored.

I have always used music to lift my mood and block out the sadness and depression. But it wasn't until my spiritual journey that I realised what a powerful self-help and motivational tool music has provided me. Music has the power to change your mood and emotions in an instant. I do remember my darkest days of depression and not wanting any music at all. Music can bring memories flooding back and can even move you to tears.

Music Therapy

You will not find any athlete that does not use music to motivate them to perform at their best. Music is used in every gym in the world! Music motivates, and I use it every chance I get to make me feel good, motivate me and lift my mood.

Through my journey to stage I certainly used it to drum up the confidence I clearly didn't have to strut around on stage. Just like affirmations, I would sing songs that would fill me with a sense of pride in myself. If I wasn't listening to affirmations in the car, I was listening to a preselected playlist of pump up songs and singing at the top of my voice!

Only recently I was going through another challenging period in life. I started watching and listening to Channel V, while I am an 80s child, I am always on the lookout for a new favourite song. When I first saw the clip for "Uptown Funk" (feat. Bruno Mars) by Mark Ronson, I stood watching transfixed. It was like the universe delivered to me the exact song I needed to support me through my latest challenge. I googled the words instantly and then downloaded the song onto my phone. That preceded weeks and weeks of having "Uptown Funk" on repeat. I would have listened to this song maybe 10,000 times plus watched the video clip dozens of times. Why? Because I love it! Because it makes me feel good. Because it makes me sing and dance. Because the lyrics are just perfect for feeling good about yourself!

Do you have a song that when you hear it makes you want to sing out loud and dance with reckless abandon? In those moments you feel fully alive, full of energy and truly happy. And all because you hear a few chords strung together in the right sequence. Music can have an enormous impact on us; it can lift your mood, put a smile on your face and add immeasurable quality to your day and life. Through my journey I realised that music is yet another tool that I use to keep me grounded in the present moment. It is a form of meditation as while my favourite song is playing and I am singing and dancing, I am not worrying about the future or beating myself up over the past.

If you are at home and you feel anxiety or depressing thoughts overwhelming you, turn on the stereo loud with your happy songs! Make yourself sing and dance! Guaranteed to lift your mood in minutes. ☺

Top Tips

- Build a collection of inspirational and motivational songs on your smart phone or iPod so you can listen to music that fills your heart with joy every single day. With the incredible range of ear buds available, you can listen to music almost anywhere. On your commute or at work if your job permits; the last thing I do before I walk out the door in the morning is put on an uplifting song to ensure I start my day with a spring in my step!

- There is not an athlete in the world who doesn't use music as part of their workout. Pick your favourite workout tracks and incorporate them into your exercise regime to motivate you to push harder!

- Share music with friends or that special someone. There is nothing like happy music in the background as you catch up with friends—aka party! I usually have one of the music channels on to watch the visual video clip as well. Or change the mood for that special someone with something more romantic or sexy!

- We have all walked into a day spa for a massage and heard that relaxing New Age music. Easy enough to put on your smartphone and time it for 20 minutes or so if you have trouble sleeping. Music can help you find your zzz's.

- Don't underestimate the power of driving along and singing at the top of your voice! Guaranteed to lift your mood! I also play music while I am doing the housework for a similar effect!

Music has played a huge role in my life in my battle with depression. I have used it to block out the world and ensure I am protected from anything sad. So many girl power songs have been played over and over and over!

*"Music speaks what cannot be expressed,
soothes the mind and gives it rest,
heals the heart and makes it whole, flows
from heaven to the soul."*

—Anon.

Give Thanks

I wasn't grateful for anything; there was nothing in life that I could find any appreciation for. That is what depression is isn't it? I was the victim and all I felt was resentment. My life seemed to be full of people that I blamed for my misery. When you are finding it hard to summon the will to live, appreciation for anything is certainly the furthest from your mind.

My childhood wasn't ideal from a loving, supportive standpoint; however, I didn't want for anything material. I went to private schools for the majority of my schooling; I was given every opportunity and more than most. I was never hungry, I always had a warm bed and my bedroom had every gadget, poster, trinket, toy or doll that is a little girl's dream. And while material things are certainly not the answer to happiness, there does seem to be a correlation between children who have all the things they want coupled with the absence of the ideal loving environment and their lack of ability to see how fortunate they are.

My lack of appreciation of anything in life continued throughout my twenties, thirties and forties, as did my depression. I was not a happy camper, and I would often receive feedback, particularly at work, of how sullen, unhappy, ungrateful and rude I appeared. Really? I was trying so hard to hide it! I had no appreciation or respect for anyone or anything; how could I when I was blinded by my own lack of self-worth? Trouble was, I had no idea that hating myself was the cause of my problems!

Attitude of Gratitude

Why do we only express gratitude at significant occasions? We thank people for wishing us a happy birthday or for a gift. For a promotion at work or on congratulations for an engagement or wedding. And then there are all the throwaway thank-yous that are part of our day but not really genuine—the checkout girl, the barista, the bank teller, the bus driver. When was the last time you actually thought about how lucky we are to be able to purchase our food so easily at a supermarket? The checkout girl is actually the last human on a very long line of people, starting at the farmer, to provide you with food that you didn't have to kill or grow. The thanks we should feel for this everyday transaction should be enormous!

The benefits of practising gratitude are well researched and documented and truly are endless. When you regularly practise gratitude and consciously take the time to notice and reflect upon the things you are thankful for, you can't help but experience positive emotions. You will also find that you cultivate more kindness and compassion, and research has suggested that you will even reduce stress, sleep better and improve your immunity!

Writing a gratitude list every day was something I was introduced to many years ago. But like meditation, affirmations, visualisations... I just went through the motions without learning the lesson. Yeah, I was thankful for the roof over my head, food in the fridge and clean running water, but I didn't for one second think about what life would be like without these things. We see homeless people on the street and know that there are people far worse off than we are, but how often do we stop and think of how truly fortunate we are? I wasn't alone in taking all our modern-day luxuries for granted. With depression being such a selfish illness, I did not have the capacity to realise.

I didn't learn this lesson until my extended unemployment a few years ago—so it was post my competitions. And while my gratitude was growing through my journey to stage, it didn't hit home until the very roof over my head was being threatened. Until I couldn't afford my groceries. Not all the heartbreak I had suffered or all the traumas of competing came close to the fear that comes from nearly losing the basics in life. I didn't have a partner or family to back me; I was totally reliant on myself, and here I was in this incredibly humbling and soul-destroying position.

I was doing a lot of reading and personal development work during this time. My journey to stage had changed me, but clearly I still needed a few more lessons and I was self-aware enough to realise this now. I read The Power by Rhonda Byrne, and if you are familiar with the law of attraction, you will know that gratitude is the number one quality you simply must cultivate if you want your life to change.

Having done all the ground work with meditation and affirmations, I was more in control of my thoughts, and I was able to apply these techniques easily.

Top Tips

- Gratitude list. I was journaling every day during this period (more on this shortly), so adding a gratitude list to this habit was easy. Every day I would write down what I was grateful for, and, yes, food in the fridge, clean running water and a roof over my head were on the lists once again. However this time I could feel the gratitude for these basic things in life surging through my veins! No longer were these basics taken for granted! And I would ensure I added some new or different ones every day. They can be as simple as thank you for a good night's sleep, thank you for my health, thank you for my awesome new job! It doesn't matter what you write as long as you feel the appreciation.

- Affirmation Cards. I dragged out the Louise Hay affirmation cards and stuck them all over the bathroom mirror as I had done to help me compete. This time, however, they were all about gratitude and my new job!
- Gratitude Attitude. Driving down the street I would thank everyone I saw. I thanked the garbage man, the gardener, the bus driver, the policeman and fireman. Everyone you see or interact with enhances your life in some way. Where would we be if the garbage man didn't do his job? Give thanks to every single person—we are all in this together, and we all rely on each other!

These are what I did; however, here are some more suggestions that may resonate with you:

- Gratitude Jar. Every time something good happens, write it on a piece of paper and put in a jar. The act of recognising that this is something worth remembering as a good thing will help you appreciate. On New Year's Eve, make a celebration out of opening the jar and reading out all the awesome things that happened to you through the year!
- Gratitude Letter. How often do we really thank the people in our life for being in our life? I am totally overwhelmed with gratitude for the people in my life who still stuck with me after the truly horrible person I used to be! So send your loved ones a lovely handwritten letter or an email or whatever you think appropriate. It doesn't have to be a special occasion; just let them know how grateful you are for their presence.

Of course, the goal is not to continually have to practise all these gratitude activities but rather to make it a default feeling within you. This will come with time, I promise! I don't do any of the above anymore, as I have trained my brain to do it automatically every day on waking and at any other idle time through my day. I am constantly overwhelmed with gratitude after doing a grocery shop or taking a shower. We are *so* blessed!

Gratitude and Water

A revolutionary study on gratitude and our health has been done by Masaru Emoto in Japan through studying water. Our bodies are made up of 70 percent water, and the human head is actually 80 percent water, so his findings have a huge impact on our understanding of how gratitude can improve our health. He exposed water to positive words and feelings such as love, gratitude and happiness by either speaking the words to the glass of water or placing a label with the word on the glass. He then examined this water under a microscope and could actually see the energy level and structure of the water change to perfectly harmonious crystal structures. The higher the positive feelings and words, the more beautiful the crystals. When he did the opposite and exposed the water to words such as hate, sadness and evil, the energy level of the water decreased and the structure became chaotic without the beautiful crystal line structure of the positive words.

If the words we choose can affect the structure of water, just think of the effect this has on our health when our bodies and cells are made up mainly of water. If we are expressing gratitude and appreciation every day, can you imagine the impact this is having on our health and bodies? This is a phenomenal discovery and highlights the importance of giving thanks for your health and your body every single day!

Thinking about, feeling about, writing about and talking about all you have to be grateful for is guaranteed to boost your happiness and overall sense of well-being. This has been researched in many, many studies. In the US and Canada they even have a celebrated holiday for Thanksgiving! It can keep you rooted in the present moment as you are expressing appreciation and can have a lasting affect as you recall the thing, event or person you are grateful for. It doesn't matter how bad your day was, there is always, always something to be grateful for!

> *"The body and mind are inextricably connected, with our thoughts and emotions exerting a powerful influence on our health."*
> —Dr Bradley Nelson
> *Food Matters*, FMTV

Journaling

Writing out all the depressing thoughts in my head was just like meditation—way too confronting for me. I was doing all I could to run away from my thoughts and feelings. Why would I want to write them down and see them on paper? And to have a record of all these thoughts to read over again? To relive my misery? How could that possibly help me?! I felt this was a negative approach to healing and it wouldn't help me.

Once again I had read about the benefits of journaling and had been advised to do this from my alternate health practitioners. But once again, I thought it was a load of hooey, and I resisted. I had never been much of a writer; I never write a to-do list or a shopping list, as I generally remember everything. I didn't have one of those secret teenage diaries, and I was not a good note taker at school. Even at work today, I remember most things. When I do write things down, I can barely read my own writing anyway! In this computer age I have lost the skill of writing beautifully as we once did.

I saw writing as a waste of time. Rather than writing about doing stuff, why not use the time to just do it?! I felt the same about writing down my goals, as I had done this exercise many times before and not achieved them. But, again, why waste time writing about it; instead, use the time to move towards your goals!

What is a Journal?

A journal is not a diary. A diary is where you record events, times and dates of actual events. A journal is where you analyze and evaluate. It encourages you to consider who you are, what you do, why you do what you do and what you have learned from it all. Some call it a form of meditation as it should be free flowing as you write the thoughts as they come up in the present moment.

Halfhearted attempts

Like with meditation and affirmations, I had made a few halfhearted attempts. But unlike meditation and affirmations, it wasn't during my journey to stage that I resurrected this one. My spiritual journey continues way beyond stage and with the depth of misery I have put myself through, I don't think my journey of learning and improving will end anytime soon! As mentioned, I found myself unemployed for many months a couple of years ago; there is nothing like the fear of not being able to afford food or the roof over your head to drive you to try anything at all to change your situation.

Morning Pages

It wasn't until I was studying with the Institute of Integrative Nutrition® that this journaling thing came back to smack me in the head. I was introduced to this morning pages concept, invented by Julia Cameron, and it resonated with me. Through my bodybuilding I had established a well-entrenched morning routine (which we will cover shortly), and with the extra time on my hands while unemployed, I started to include journaling into my morning routine.

Mornings are the ideal time to set the scene for the day and get grounded and focused. It is a beautiful time of the day as it is a new day! And anything can happen in just one day, right? It's an opportunity to start afresh and leave the negativity of yesterday behind. Journaling can assist with this. Yeah, I didn't believe it either but stay with me.

Have you ever had a sleepless night, tossing and turning and going over and over things you said or did not say, decisions you made that you regret—if I had done this then that wouldn't have happened—or whatever you have got going on in your head that is a continual loop? I have spent countless nights doing this over the years. Low self-worth ensures you are constantly worried about what others think of you, and with my inability to communicate effectively, I was always replaying over and over…. Whatever it is you have got looping, it is from the past, so there is little value in wasting your precious energy and head space on reliving a scene that you can't change. The past is just a story you keep telling yourself in your head—we have covered this! And then when morning comes you drag yourself out of bed and start the day tired, and, low and behold, the same loop thoughts are still running through your head! God, give me a break!

So the idea with morning pages is as soon as you wake have your journal and pen by your bed and just start writing. Write it all out—no one else will read it. Some of the things I have written I can't even understand what I have written!! Particularly as so often I was writing through tears. It doesn't matter. Get it out on paper, write whatever topic comes to mind. I can't really explain it, but the moment you take that loopy thought and write it down, it just feels weird to keep looping it in your head. You allow your brain to cut through all the wasted cycles and make better use of your thoughts, and it will allow your mind to be naturally drawn towards what is more important, like creating a life you love! And if you need a good cry, well, isn't it a good idea to get it out of the way at the beginning of the day?

The other thing about writing down your thoughts is that you tend to ask yourself questions as to why you are feeling or thinking like this, approach it from a different angle and understand the events in a different way. This will give you a better perspective in general about circumstances in life.

Basically you are getting everything in your head that may have stopped a peaceful night's sleep out of your head! Don't worry about spelling, punctuation or grammar, just write and write until there is no more. You don't even need to go back and read it; in fact, I would recommend you don't. What's the point of rehashing a data dump of negativity? This was a revelation to me; of course I don't need to reread it!

As soon as the pen pauses on the data dump, I tend to add in a gratitude list as per the previous chapter. Starting off the day with gratitude is so important! There are so many things to be grateful for, even if you don't feel it. Check your pulse! That's a good one to start with! The bed you just spent the night in, the warm blanket, the roof over your head—make them as simple or as lavish as you like, but find at least five things to be grateful for every day. Can't think of anything new to be grateful for? Rewrite the same ones from yesterday, but make sure you are focusing on gratitude for something.

After you have been doing this for a while, you will start to use this tool in a more positive, creative way. Many use morning pages to ensure they achieve their goals in life and rewrite their goals each day. It really is a form of meditation, and you will find that inspiring thoughts will come up not only when you are writing but during the day. It is a tool used for many purposes, and I encourage you to use it to improve all areas of your life.

Top Tips

- Buy yourself a beautiful inspiring journal and pen, rather than using a scrappy old notebook. Start the process off with tools that are going to cultivate inspiration and positive feelings.
- Choose an inspiring place to write, particularly if you are not comfortable writing in front of your partner in bed. Pick a spot in your home that relaxes you, motivates you—a big comfy chair, by a nice view from your window. Again, set the scene to cultivate inspiration and positive feelings.
- Write about an event that is troubling you in the third person. This can provide distance and a different perspective.
- Include motivational quotes. I am huge on quotes and use them to motivate me every day

(from Pinterest). Pick quotes that resonate with you and write (and rewrite) them in your journal.

- Gratitude list. Always include something that you are grateful for either at the beginning or at the end of your daily log.
- Write stream of consciousness. Don't edit your thoughts or feelings; write them as they come up with no comment or judgement.
- Keep it secure. This is very personal and is for you only, unless you choose to share it. It is important to feel comfortable in writing freely any thoughts that you may not be comfortable sharing with anyone.
- Don't worry if you miss a day. We all miss a day, but try and make it a habit of doing it on most days. You could even try it at night as well to clear your thoughts before sleep if that suits you better.

Maintaining a journal can be one of the best personal growth activities you can undertake. Writing is a tremendous way to get to know yourself from the inside and develop self-awareness. It will also help you clarify intentions and become creative. It's like a one-on-one with your boss; Yes, you are your own boss! For me, writing is part of my healing journey. My blogs have gone unread by many; however, they have served a tremendous purpose for me!

"Buy a notebook. Write down what you want. Write down what hurts you. Show it to someone you love. Save it for your children. Burn it in the backyard. Either way go to bed knowing that in some way, those things are out of you."

—Anon.

Mainstream Media

I grew up in the age when television was a brand-new concept. I started off with black and white, and I can remember the excitement when colour was introduced in the 1970s. Only free to air back then and we were limited to three commercial channels and the ABC. As a product of this new media phenomenon, I, of course, was glued to the screen whenever I was allowed. Certain TV shows became a must-see every night or week. Back then shows were very conservative; The Sullivans was my favourite! Happy Days, I Dream of Jeannie, and Bewitched. You only have to look at these shows and compare to what is on TV today to get an idea of how society has changed its values.

TV became a way of life for most. My mother was fairly strict, but it still seemed to be on most of the time we were at home and through dinner time. Always easier for my dysfunctional family to watch a TV show together than actually have a conversation! And with only one TV in the house, it always seemed to be a source of arguments of what to watch! I used to argue with my mother every Sunday night—I just had to watch Countdown, which was on at six, our dinnertime. And of course, rock music was not something that my mother was a fan of, being a professional classical musician.

After leaving home, TV just became a part of my nightly routine; I was certainly not unique! Whether it be the latest addictive fictional drama or watching the news, I was brought up in an age where what you saw on TV replaced reading and researching any topic. It had to be true if it was on TV, right? Watching TV dominated our life and had become a daily habit. Without the Internet, it was our only way to connect with the outside world.

Research on the TV Phenomenon

Here are some interesting observations on the effect watching TV has had on our lives.

Health
There are numerous studies that draw direct parallels with obesity, poor eating habits and watching TV. I know I have been guilty of sitting on the couch mindlessly eating while watching and suddenly the whole packet has gone! And how about this: There is no time to cook a healthy meal because my favourite show starts in 10 minutes. I look at myself now, and I can't believe I ever did that!

Distraction
It distracts us from real people. Have you been chatting to a friend on the phone only to realise your favourite show is about to start and so excuse yourself? Characters on TV are not real, and yet they have been cleverly designed to be more interesting than talking to friends and family? TV also distracts you from yourself; TV is an escape, and I used it for many, many, many years to escape from how much I hated my life.

Spending
Corporations spend millions on advertising through all forms of the media not on the hope that they will influence our spending, they know they will! Often Advertising campaigns twist facts so far from the truth, and sadly we believe them! I am sure I am not alone in being sucked in to buying from Danoz Direct.

Satisfaction
According to studies, those that watch TV every night report less satisfaction with life, higher materialistic aspirations and more anxiety. Let's face it: where do we get our ideals of what a beautiful woman looks like? We are constantly comparing ourselves to people in the media instead of focusing on ourselves and our lives. I am guilty again.

Intimacy
Couples who have a TV in the bedroom have sex half as often as those who don't. I wonder if my marriage would have survived if my husband wasn't always glued to the TV.

Sensationalism The media is business, big business! Just the same as advertising campaigns, stories on the news and current affairs are dramatized to suck you in— "Can't miss episode" or "show of the year". They play on your fear of missing out! Added to that, the facts are twisted and manipulated in order to grab your attention and make you watch their channel. Why is it we believe whatever we are told by *A Current Affair* without doing our own research?

Depression Had been my constant companion all my life. Do I really need to know about the old lady who was bashed and robbed? As sad as it is, hearing about it is not only depressing, it installs fear. I can get depressed all by myself! I don't need outside help to make me feel worse! It's no coincidence then when the media air a story about the latest flu epidemic that all of a sudden doctors and hospitals are flooded with new patients. And it is no coincidence that the Paris hostage situation occurred so soon after Martin Place in Sydney. We are all connected by energy, and if you tap into this universal negative energy generated by the latest news story you may just attract some of this negativity to your own life.

Media-free Diet

I don't think I realised the influence of the media on my attitude, thoughts, mood, opinion, time, health and spending until I eliminated it from the majority of my life. I didn't make a snap decision; in fact, I don't think I ever made a conscious decision. I did make a decision not to watch the news anymore from recommendations from my alternate healers and in more recent years extended this further. With the advent of pay TV, I could really select shows that were enhancing my well-being rather than just watch for the sake of watching.

On my journey to stage the first time, especially in the last six weeks when I wasn't working, my focus was 100 percent on my training, my diet and all the techniques I am sharing with you to find self-confidence and work on my mind. No TV was a no-brainer! Unless I was watching *Rocky*! ☺

I haven't watched mainstream television for ten years. I have not watched the news for even longer. Have I missed out on anything earth shattering? No. I hear about dramatic, world-changing events in my Facebook news feed! Do I feel better about life when I am not hooked in to the latest drama on TV? *Yes!*

Top Tips

- Be more intentional about filling in your time. Have a family meal and actually talk to each other. Take the time to cook a gourmet meal. Go for a walk or talk to a friend. Go to the gym, find a new hobby, read or study; create positive habits that contribute to your development and the pursuit of your dreams.
- Adopt a "less is more" attitude. You don't have to eliminate all TV! I am not suggesting a complete blackout. Be selective of the shows you watch and watch only those shows; try and make them educational. If you find yourself surfing and looking for something to watch, it is time to find a new hobby!
- Reduce the number of TVs. When I grew up we had one TV. Now it seems normal to have three or four! Why?
- Be patient. It will get easier. Like any habit, the more you do it, the easier it gets. When you start filling in the time with more meaning, life will become more meaningful.

Change is hard. But some changes have a greater benefit and impact on all areas of your life than others. Watching less television and switching off from the media in general just may be your quickest shortcut to a healthier, more relaxed way of living.

"Every thought we think and every word we speak is creating our future."
—You Can Health Your Life
Food Matters, FMTV

Social Media

M y 10-year anniversary on Facebook recently passed. I can remember in the beginning being absolutely transfixed to this new phenomenon. For a girl that grew up without the Internet or mobile phones, this was truly an amazing way to keep in touch with friends all over the world. I logged in every single day for nearly 10 years! I even had allocated time in each day that was my Facebook time and would make sure I saw everything in my newsfeed (or so I thought). If I didn't have time to do this, I felt like I was missing out, that life was happening without me.

Being an introvert, I didn't share much about my own life. More of a stalker than a talker! With my journey to stage, however, I watched my new circle of fitness friends post selfies and progress shots. I did post a few myself and began to learn about the comment and like factor of Facebook. If I didn't get many, it didn't feel great.

When I started my business page in 2014, I began to understand the importance of comments and likes. I would spend hours composing carefully worded posts to have Facebook only show my posts to a handful of people. (When you have a business page, you can see how many newsfeeds your post appears in) Without engagement—aka comments and likes—Facebook ignores my posts and limits their visibility. I have to pay Facebook money to ensure my posts are seen! So even Facebook endorses the "must be popular" factor to ensure visibility.

Recently after yet another major negative event that the media cleverly provoked emotions and a frenzy of opinions, I began to realise that Facebook was becoming another platform for this negative influence on me. I don't have to watch the news as I only need scroll through my Facebook feed to find out what is going on and, worse, that we are even more influenced by the media that we now feel the need to voice our opinion on hot topics that the media have chosen to sensationalise to attract viewers. Aren't we just regurgitating the opinion of the media? There are always two sides to every story; do we ever research other aspects of the story before voicing our view? Or do we just believe what the TV journalists present?

Unlike my divorce from mainstream media from the previous chapter, I made a conscious decision that I would stop voicing my own misguided opinion on news events, limit my posting on Facebook, and only log in to answer private messages. When I grew up I used to ride my bike to my friend's place to catch up or pick up the phone to actually speak to my friends. How have we slipped into this virtual relationship with our friends and family? Am I just getting old? Are these old-fashioned values gone forever?

Just like giving up mainstream media, I had no idea the impact that social media was having on me until I removed it from my life. The personal growth and time I have discovered since has truly transformed my life!

Here is what I have learned from my Facebook-free life:

Time and Space

The universe loves space; it creates a vacuum to be filled, and depending on where you are in your journey of personal growth you will find inspiration of how to fill in this time. Hopefully not with TV... but spend that hour a day you used to spend on Facebook in the real world instead. Read a book. Talk to a friend. Play with your pet. Go for a walk. Bake a cake. Cook a gourmet meal. Volunteer. Find a new hobby. Enrol in a short course. Study. Join a Meetup group and make new friends. Make a list of your goals and work towards them. I realise that many use their commute to log into Facebook, but even this time can be used more productively, can't it? Listen to a podcast or an inspirational speaker. Grab that book off your shelf you've been meaning to read. I was led to further my knowledge and education on a subject that I had been ignoring for too long; a whole new world and future has opened up for me and I am so excited!

True Friends We seem to have created more online friends than real-life friends. Are we all caught up in some virtual game? Maybe I am showing my age again, but surely talking with, meeting up with, seeing in the flesh friends are more valuable than people who only comment on your photo of your breakfast or your latest check-in. your true friends will make time for you outside Facebook and won't rely on status updates to find out about your life. Why do we put these virtual friends before the true friends in our life? And why is it that some friends make drastic assumptions of what your life is like based on a few random posts? is everything we post on Facebook now assumed to be the summation of our life?

Self-worth Facebook can have a huge impact on your self-esteem if you are reliant on likes and comments to your posts. What's worse is Facebook only rewards you with more visibility for your posts depending on the number of likes you get! so it's no wonder we base our sense of self or popularity on how many likes we get. isn't this constantly seeking approval from others? doesn't this promote unhealthy competition? Why is it some people keep reposting their popular photos of themselves so we see it again so they can receive a new round of likes and comments? do they need constant reinforcement from the same photo? I am very glad I grew up without Facebook—so much additional pressure for teenagers! to look good, to have the latest fashion, to be slim.. give up the need to participate in the self-promotion rat race. Focus on yourself, and stop comparing yourself to everyone in your newsfeed.

Sense of Calm The quieter you become, the more you can hear. We spend a tremendous amount of time distracting ourselves from ourselves. the TV or radio is always on, and then we log into Facebook to further distract ourselves. But aren't we distracting ourselves from our own life? Is our own life so boring or not worth our attention that we need to escape into a virtual world? It is amazing what inspiration comes to mind when you allow silence to become a part of your life. If you are constantly distracted, how will you come up with that great new idea? There is so much noise out there! When you choose to limit the amount of influence it has on you and put your peace of mind ahead of keeping updated on what so and so did for the weekend, your life will become calmer, more peaceful and less stressful!

Let go of the Past

Facebook can be a terrific tool to connect with long, lost friends and to stay connected to friends and family all over the world. However, we all have skeletons in the closet; ask yourself what good it does to stay connected to people who have had a negative impact on you or your life. How do you feel when you see something in your newsfeed from an old boyfriend or girlfriend? Do we really need to carry around 1,000 odd friends with us for the rest of our lives? How many people on your friends list do you really want to still be friends with? I have no problem in defriending those I don't feel enrich my life in a positive way. Life is always changing; we are always changing and growing. Nothing stands still. Let go of the past and focus on the present!

Top Tips

- Friend list audit. Ask yourself if you would want to keep this connection in the real world. Examine the benefits of keeping the connection and unfriend if appropriate. If you are not ready to take this step and their posts don't have a positive impact on you, then simply unfollow. Their posts will not appear in your newsfeed. you can then still be Facebook friends without knowing all the details of their life. And they won't even know!

- Purge your Liked Pages. If you go into Pages and then Liked Pages, you can see all the pages you have liked. Again examine the positive or negative impact each page has on you when you see posts from this page. If you are no longer interested or their posts are not contributing to your happiness or education, then simply unlike.

- Prioritise your newsfeed. Facebook now has the facility to select 30 pages that you want to see first in your newsfeed. Select the ones that inspire you, lift you higher, motivate you, bring you happiness or extend your knowledge on a favorite subject. design your own newsfeed to what you want rather than leaving it all up to the randomness and bias of Facebook.
- Maintain some mystery. I am truly shocked at the detail of people's lives they share on Facebook. Now I may be showing my age again, but surely being a bit mysterious is an attractive quality. Sharing major events is great, but the daily pictures and posts of what others ate for breakfast or what happened on their trip to or from work? I know I have better things to do with my time than witness these events. Then there are the more personal posts that really have me scratching my head. It seems to me that in the effort to gain more and more attention and validation they just lose more and more respect.

There is no doubt that Facebook is a wonderful tool for staying connected and sharing news and photos easily. There are plenty of positives, but in an age where low self-esteem is rampant and we struggle with time to cook good food and exercise, is it really a productive use of time?

"Your life isn't yours if you constantly seek out and care what others think of you."
—Anon.

Read More Books

L ike music, I didn't realise the importance of reading until recently. I always did a lot of reading, but I didn't apply what I was learning! So was I really learning? Being a big reader comes with being an introvert to me. But I did use books as another means of escape from my head and my life. Most of us have had that book we just couldn't put down! And then when it is finished you feel a little lost until you find the next book to bury yourself into.

Escaping from life, whether it be through a good novel or TV, is not necessarily a bad thing, as long as you are doing it for relaxation. As with everything in life, balance is key.

I was never a good student; I resented the curriculum and didn't feel an interest in any of my subjects other than music or sport. And the whole committing everything to memory on topics that I had zero interest saw me only scraping through my exams. I do understand that for certain professions you need to know everything without reference but I really resented the exam method of testing knowledge. I had no intentions of being a heart surgeon!

So I walked out of school, I never went to university much to my mother's horror, happily throwing away all my books and believing that I had done my time on this learning rubbish. Did I really think all I learned in school about algebra and trigonometry was enough to get me through life? Why is it that so many of us think our learning is over once we have finished our formal qualifications? For some professions you have to continually keep updated to maintain your professional status and jobs, which is great, but what about life skills, like dealing with heartache, depression, finances, death, parenthood and self-love? Where do we learn these skills?

We Learn When We are Ready!

I had read hundreds of self-development books trying to find the cause of my misery. With every book I would say to myself, *this is the one that will provide the answers.* The problem is that if you are not in the right head and heart space to receive the message the book is sending you, it won't resonate. Even when my alternate healers were giving me the same advice, I wasn't ready. We all get there in our own time and more often than not we can't be told by someone else. All the answers are actually within us—yeah, I didn't believe that one for a very long time either!—and it is through our spiritual journey that we come to a place of awareness. I have actually gone back and reread a number of my books, and now they make perfect sense!

But how do you know when you are ready? You keep on reading until you find something that resonates and inspires you to take action. We don't stop learning until the day we die, and we shouldn't be so arrogant to think that we are ever too old to learn something new.

Have you ever thought why big, wealthy houses always have a library? Having a library in the house was considered a status of the rich and successful because they knew that continually reading and educating yourself is crucial to being happy, rich and successful!

Why did the Nazis burn books? Knowledge expands the mind. Knowledge is freedom.

Top Tips

- Carry a book with you. You never know when you will be caught having to wait for a meeting, appointment, friend or whatever. Instead of mindlessly checking Facebook, feed your mind with some new information to uplift, motivate, inspire and educate.

- Utilise your commute time. I always hear people complain how long their commute time is, and yet this is the time I utilise every day to read either a book or blogs on subjects I want to know more about. Make this so-called wasted time every day into productive time.

- Having trouble getting to sleep? I find reading in bed the best way to bring on sleep. And if you are utilising this time to do affirmations and visualisations, the last thing you are reading as you drift off will imprint on your subconscious mind, as we have discussed in previous chapters.

- Replace TV or social media time with reading. That was how my grandparents used to spend every evening! Have a special reading recliner in the living room, make yourself a nice cup of tea, and sit back and enjoy!

- Worried about cost? I buy my books second hand through eBay or other websites that recycle books. Unless it is a masterpiece I know I will want to read again, once I have read it, I resell or donate it to a local charity.

- Prefer to listen to a book? In the smartphone age, it is easier than ever to actually listen to a book rather than read it. We all take in information and learn differently, so if you are an auditory learner, you can listen while you walk!

So many people only read a handful of books after they finish school and university, and, yet, in these times of rapid change, ideas are the very commodity of success. All it takes is one idea from one book to make a million, to change your perspective on a relationship, to totally transform your life, so why aren't we all continually reading?

"No matter how busy you may think you are, you must find time for reading or surrender yourself to self-chosen ignorance."

—Confucius

Home Haven

My entire life I have wanted to be happily married, have children—the whole white picket fence dream. Not only did I want to make up for the unhappiness of my own childhood, but the pressure from society to achieve this and to "do" life in the right order (man/marry/house/kids) was overwhelming and was one of the main causes of my depression. I was single and childless and felt that I had failed in life.

My second marriage came with a beautiful little house that I adored. I spent my entire weekend gardening, painting, redecorating, cleaning and working on my gorgeous home. I simply love creating a home. I was happy despite being with the wrong man who didn't feel the same about homemaking as I do. When my marriage broke down and the house had to be sold, my devastation was equal over the loss of the house and the relationship.

When I lost my dream home, I then proceeded to care little for my living arrangements. I moved into a tiny, one-bedroom unit in an old house that had been split up into three units. I called it the hovel—it was so horrible to live in. But it matched my depression and disrespect for myself and my life. I will never forget my mother coming to visit me in this place—a mother who had the same love of creating a home as I do and who I rarely saw cry. As she walked through the door, she burst into tears. I was too depressed and out drinking most nights to register my surroundings, but clearly it was not healthy for me!

I did purchase a unit after that and tried to reignite my home love with renovations, but I was just too depressed and hating myself and life too much. I didn't even finish the renovations. I then sold it and proceeded to rent and move regularly, hoping to find happiness in the next shoebox—a term I constantly used to describe the cramped living quarters of the one-bedroom units in inner Sydney that were all I could afford.

Creating a Sanctuary

I had read about the importance of your home space in many books, and my alternate healers had also mentioned it. I so loved going into the home of my energetic healer, and it was here I began to find the inspiration to create a sanctuary of my own. Not sure I would find this inspiration in a therapist's office.

I had purposely turned my back on an important part of myself simply because I couldn't have the house. Don't get me wrong; I wasn't living in squalor! My living environment was not bad; I still cleaned and it was presentable. I just didn't go out of my way and didn't have any personal pride or love for my home simply because it was a shoebox and not a house!

Creating a space where you can retreat and rejuvenate, a space that nurtures and nourishes you, that inspires and relaxes you, that you can be yourself in and that helps you feel good is so incredibly important to your enjoyment of life. It doesn't matter if it is a house, a unit or even just your bedroom, if you share. If you don't feel good about yourself and your life, it will show in how you choose your surroundings.

Top Tips

- Make your bed. It seems obvious for some, but when you really don't care about living, why would you bother? It really says a lot about your state of mind if you can't spare two minutes to make your bed in the morning. Doesn't it feel nicer and calmer to come home at the end of the day and crawl into a made bed?
- Candles. Why do we only associate candlelight with a romantic dinner for two? or only drag them out for special occasions? life is a special

---

occasion! The flicker of candlelight brings a very relaxing, cosy atmosphere, and with fragrant ones the room is filled with a glorious scent. I don't think you can ever have enough candles, and I have them in every room.

- Essential oils. Or incense or whatever takes your fancy to fill your living space with your favourite scent. I would steer away from commercial air fresheners and plug ins. They are loaded with chemicals and increase your toxic load. Lavender is well known for its relaxing properties and to help you sleep.

- Fairy lights. I love fairy lights! I have them all over my balcony, and as they are solar powered, they light up every night, which I just love! They don't just need to be outdoors, either. You can put them around your bathroom mirror, your bed, a window or anywhere!

- Lamps. I am not a fan of overhead lights and prefer a lamp in every room instead. I have had a Himalayan Salt Lamp on my wish list for ages for its healing qualities. Any decorative lamp that adds a nice subdued lighting to the room.

- De-clutter. A cluttered space makes for a cluttered brain! I learnt a long time ago when you are living in a shoebox you just can't afford to hoard things or to not put things away. And if I can't find a home for it, then it has to go in the bin! It only takes a moment to file or throw away the mail each day, do the dishes and put your clothes and shoes away.

- Colours. My favourite colour is green, which is a calming colour. I try and keep the colour scheme in earthy tones of green and brown which resonates with me.

- Music. Music is nearly always playing, as I don't watch TV. It can calm me, excite me, motivate me and make me smile!

- Textiles. Cushions and throw rugs are mandatory for me on the lounge and my bedroom. I like nice sheets, too.
- Books. You can tell a lot about someone by the books they keep. My bookshelf will certainly tell you all about me! Books make a house a home in my opinion. I read constantly and have a big bookshelf of ones that are important to me. When I am stuck for something to read, I stand there and wait for one to speak to me. Some I have reread six times!
- Plants and flowers. I have a green thumb and I simply love gardening. I get this from my mother and grandmother, which is one of the many reasons I was so bitter about my shoebox living. But it doesn't matter how you live—you can still have plants! My balcony always has flowers and herbs and special plants for my feline best friend.
- Things you love. From photos to paintings to mementos to whatever means something to you that makes you feel good! Decorate your home with what brings you joy.

Two years ago I once again moved into my own unit. Yes, it is another one bedder, but I have dropped the derogatory term. I put in new blinds, carpet and painted before I moved in, with a feature wall that is a beautiful green colour. With all of the above incorporated into my home, I truly love walking through the door every night!

"Your home is your sanctuary.
Take care of this and your life becomes
all that you wish it to be."

—Anon

Start the Day Well

Mornings are always the hardest when you are suffering from depression. You wake up, and for a nano second you are still in mindless sleep. Then reality hits you, your heart sinks and you wish you hadn't woken up at all. The effort it takes to simply get out of bed is enormous as that requires facing the world which you hate. I was never a good sleeper and always needed a drug of some sort to ensure I did sleep, so I was not a fan of mornings, although I was never a fan of Doona (duvet) days, either. Why would I want to spend more time in bed trying to sleep and managing that monkey in my head? I would rather get up and use all my other destructive behaviors to avoid my thoughts. I was also not much of a sickie bludger; despite all my issues, having a job is what prevented me from going completely under. I had responsibility at work. People relied on me at work. I was expected to be there, so it gave me the only sense of purpose and belonging.

But I was still very slow in the morning due to the substance hangover and the lack of love of the day ahead or life in general. I would drag myself out of bed late, rush to get ready, skip breakfast or eat on the run and leave in complete disarray just in time to get to the office. Just the thought of how I used to start my day stresses me!

Set the Scene

The start of the day sets the scene for the day; we have all heard this before. Or the other well-known saying of "I woke up on the wrong side of the bed this morning" to excuse yourself for messy, unproductive and everything-seems-to-be-going-wrong mornings or days. The right morning routine can not only instill a sense of purpose and peace but will give you the foundation to handle whatever the day throws at you. It can also ensure you are moving towards your goals in life, and many health goals have a very firm place in the mornings. It makes sense that I didn't have a morning routine for so many years as I didn't have any goals, purpose or peace! When you are just in survival mode, mornings are a period of time to get over.

Once again, if you ask any successful person in the world they will have a morning routine. Do enough research and you will discover that all personal development gurus recommend the same. There is a firm connection between getting up early, developing a morning routine and success. My routine was not from copying anyone in particular, and I didn't purposefully set out to create a morning routine. It was born out of the need to accommodate my new bodybuilding lifestyle; if I was going to get up on stage, I had to change my daily routine. And when I now look at my morning rituals, there is a common thread with successful people, so I must be doing something right!

Top Tips

- Wake up early. Nearly all successful people wake up early; why is that? The energy of the new day as the sun rises is truly magical. It's a time of day when you can seek out peace and quiet, get a head start, get organized, get healthier and increase energy. There are numerous studies that say getting up early will make you happier, increase your productivity and creativity. Start with 5 mins earlier for a few weeks and then increase to 10 mins and so on until you reach your goal wake up time.
- Meditate. Mornings are the perfect time before everyone else is awake to sit quietly and

meditate for 10 minutes. Clear your mind and get ready for the day, guaranteed to start your day off with peace rather than stress!

- Write in your journal. Journaling can help you get rid of the loop thoughts that have been going through your mind over night. Get them down on paper and get them out of your head!

- Gratitude. It is such a privilege to be alive, and every morning when we wake up is a perfect opportunity to be grateful for waking up! Either run through all the things that you are grateful for in your head or write a gratitude list in your journal. Starting your day off with gratitude is a scientifically proven way to improve your mood and day!

- Exercise. Most professional athletes in the world train in the morning. There are scientifically proven benefits of exercising in the morning over any other time of the day. I used to always go to the gym after work and then for a period of time at lunch. Now I wouldn't train at any other time of the day than mornings. If the gym is not your thing, try yoga or Thai Chi or a walk.

- Get organized. Write your to-do list if you are into that, pack up your food and clothes for the day, set your intentions and plan ahead for the day's activities.

- Avoid media of any type. We are bombarded from technology every second of the day. Start your day off without any distractions and be present in the now before you day begins. Whatever news happened overnight you can find out later in the day. Try and avoid the negativity of the media first thing. Or at all!

- Go for a walk in nature and watch the sunrise! Now that's a great way to start the day. ☺

"How you begin your day can make your day or break your day. Your attitude and your actions have a strong effect on your whole day. Begin with a smile, a calmness of mind and heart filled with gratitude. A positive mindset that it's going to be a wonderful day!"

—Anon

What Do You Believe?

I believed life was miserable and hard. I believed I had been hard done by with my childhood, parents, parents' divorce, interrupted schooling, blah, blah, blah. Everyone has a sob story. I had the belief that I was the victim, and despite all these events being ancient history, I continued to carry them fresh in my mind (largely due to rehashing them through traditional therapy) and blame others for why my life wasn't as I wanted it to be. Life is tough and then you die. I am sure you have heard this before, and that is what I believed and is the way I lived my life. And life just kept on proving to me that I was right!

My belief about my body and my health was driven solely on appearances. I believed I was healthy purely because I was not overweight—not realising that underweight is not healthy either. I also believed that without my looks I had nothing else going for me. I was obsessed with being skinny. I was obsessed with keeping my youthful skin. I literally hung on to them for dear life.

I also believed I was nothing without a man—that I couldn't achieve anything as a single woman. So if I lost my appearance and I was single, there really was no reason to go on. I can't believe I ever thought that! But I did for a very long time. And as a firm belief in my mind, life just kept on throwing up circumstances and situations that proved my belief to be the truth for me.

What are Beliefs?
Beliefs are simply repeated thoughts with strong feelings attached to them like, "I catch colds easily" or "My stomach

is always sensitive." How about, "Coffee keeps me awake" or "I find it hard to lose weight" or "I always suffer from jetlag." All these are beliefs that you hold, but if you ask someone else (like me), none of these are true. I choose to believe differently. Yes, beliefs are a choice, believe it or not. A belief is literally what you have made up in your mind to be true; you are the judge and the jury and the verdict is in. You have left no room for negotiation. Our beliefs about any subject literally run our lives, and they will always be true. Some beliefs are conscious and we are aware of what we believe; however, the ones that can cause the most damage are the unconscious ones. Stay with me.

Money is always a good example. Did you grow up in a household where you were constantly reminded that money doesn't grow on trees? That money is hard to come by, that you have to work long hours to earn money and still there isn't enough? I know I did. I was constantly reminded of how much I was costing my mother! I can remember having to wear second hand uniforms to my exclusive all girls private school and not feeling good at all! As we become adults and are then in a position to earn our own money, we carry the same beliefs. You probably still have the same beliefs. And, yet, how is that so many millionaires make money while they sleep? Money comes easy to them. How is that millionaires pop up through a recession? You will probably say they are just lucky. But I am sure you have heard stories of lottery winners or even famous Hollywood stars who somehow lose every penny. Are they just unlucky? I am sure they didn't want to lose all their money! They simply still have the same unconscious scarcity beliefs about money, so it doesn't matter how much money they win or earn, they will lose it again through unexpected expenses.

Another example. Have you ever heard of the old Aboriginal ritual of Pointing the Bone or Boning? It is a tradition in Aboriginal tribes that an elder of the tribe will point a bone at one of the tribal members for punishment or vengeance. This is done as a ceremony with only senior elders present as witnesses while one of the elders would literally point a bone at the offender. This is a very old aboriginal custom that means that if you have the bone pointed at you, you will die. Even though the villain may be youthful and healthy, if the bone is pointed at him he dies within weeks— sometimes within days. Because this is a legendary custom of the aboriginal culture, this is a strongly held belief. The power of your mind is beyond your comprehension!

The placebo effect in medicine is another proof of the power of belief. Most of us have heard the stories of the group of patients who are not given the real pills or treatment and another group that does and, yet, the placebo group often experience significant improvements.

What you continually give to your body in the form of the running commentary in your head, aka your beliefs—and add strong feelings to those beliefs—you must receive in your body and life.

What Are Your Beliefs about Your Body and Health?

What does it mean to be truly healthy? Do you believe that being healthy is simply not being sick? Or like I used to believe, is being healthy just being skinny? If you are just feeling okay or average, is this being healthy? Do you believe it is hard to lose weight? Do you believe that aging means you will pack on the weight and the body will deteriorate? I believe I never get sick, and guess what? I never get sick. I haven't had a cold for 10 years! Now that I have achieved premium health through bodybuilding, which has further extended my beliefs, let me tell you what I now believe and feel every day as to what being healthy is.

Do you remember when you were a child or even watching your own children, how they are simply bursting with energy every day? Their bodies are light and flexible, and they move with a spring in their step. Their minds are clear, and they are constantly curious and asking questions wanting more information. They are generally happy and free of worry and stress. They sleep soundly and peacefully most nights, and they wake up refreshed. They are passionate and excited about every new day. This is how I feel! This is what feeling truly healthy is all about for me, and I experience it every day! I certainly do not believe that aging affects my weight; I am living proof of that!

Every belief and feeling you have saturates every cell and organ in your entire body. When you feel happy and positive, you are feeding your body these loving feelings and you will receive good health. When you feel stressed, worried, angry or depressed, the tension causes your nerves and cells to contract. The chemical reaction within these cells has to change as a result. This can result in dis-ease or the body not being at ease over a long period of time because of negative beliefs and feelings!

Whatever you believe about your body, your cells also believe. They don't have the ability for logical reason, so they don't question what you think, feel or believe. They hear every thought, feeling and belief you have. Your cells exist solely to serve you and keep you alive, so like dutiful soldiers, they will carry out your instructions. If you think and feel that it is hard to lose weight and that you have a weight problem, they will follow your command and ensure that what you believe is true for you.

So How Do You Change Your Beliefs?

Isn't that the million dollar question! This is one of the hardest things, and it is one I continually work on. I have nailed the right beliefs for my health, but I have a long way to go on relationships and money. Many of the tools I have described in this book will assist you, but it is important to do a bit of housework in the belief room of your mind.

Top Tips

- Identify the limiting belief that is holding you back. It is a sobering realisation that actually you are the one that is holding you back from achieving your goals. Articulate the belief that is limiting your potential.
- Consider how it impacts your life. What are you missing out on? Look at what is not working in your life right now; what are your beliefs around this?
- Ask yourself where it originates. This is a tough one. Think about your parents, siblings, childhood experiences, school friends and messages from the media. Partner, teachers or anyone who has had influence over you or where you have been taught this belief.
- Reflect on how your life will change if you change this belief. If you believed that losing weight was easy, how would this change your life? How would you feel?
- Find ways to disprove your belief. This is the most important step. Deliberately research and find others who have achieved what you want to achieve or who have overcome obstacles and changed their beliefs and their life. I believe that being healthy and maintaining a healthy weight is easy, so tapping into my mindset will definitely assist you!

"Whatever you hold in your mind will tend to occur in your life. If you continue to believe what you have always believed, you will continue to act as you have always acted. If you continue to act as you have always acted, you will continue to get what you have always gotten. If you want different results in your life, all you have to do is change your mind."

—Anon

Passion

I spent 46 years not really knowing what my passion in life was. I had read that your passion has everything to do with you and not other people, but I didn't believe it. All I wanted was a relationship and family of my own, and I believed that this was my passion in life. When I looked at myself outside the attachment to the white picket fence dream, I had an inkling it had to do with fitness. Despite my years and years of depression, I still managed to drag myself to the gym. Going to the gym truly was the only constant in my life, other than my corporate career. Strange, as exercising is said to alleviate depression. Imagine how bad I could have been if I wasn't exercising! Like my continual search for how to fix myself, I was always combing courses offered by community colleges or TAFE to see if something resonated with the hope that maybe a new career would bring me happiness. I have started many, many courses only to drop out.

They say that you have to look at what you simply love doing to find what your passion is. I hated life, so there really wasn't anything I loved doing other than getting drunk or stoned to escape my life! My motivation to go the gym was purely vanity, I can assure you. What a waste to live through all my youth and half my adult life and not know what it felt like to feel the exhilaration of doing something where time stands still (there is that present moment thing again), where you are totally absorbed in the moment, to feel truly alive, to find that deeper meaning and reward in life. When you are depressed, you don't even think these feelings are possible outside the bedroom.

What is Passion?

Many would say that passion only comes from sex! But isn't enjoyable, loving sex exhilarating? Time stands still, and you are totally absorbed in the moment and truly alive. Can there be something else in life that provides you with all of that and yet you have your clothes on?!

Passion as described in the dictionary is any powerful or compelling emotion or feeling. A strong or extravagant fondness, enthusiasm or desire for anything.

What we are passionate about is no accident. Many would say it is your calling in life. Some lucky people are born knowing or discover their passion through school. That would be another recommendation of mine, to change the school curriculum! If you mold your career around your passion, you will never work a day in your life. I am sure you have heard this statement before. But most of us, me included, have fallen into a career that we are good at and pays the bills; however, it is far from fulfilling and will eventually see you tired, stressed, anxious, frustrated, overweight, unhealthy or depressed.

This is all well and good, but when there are bills to pay and with all the other demands of life, changing direction seems impossible. How do you find the time?

My Story Continues

I finally made it to stage for my first competition. Despite all of the work I had done on myself to satisfy my ego and vanity, my journey was only just beginning. Here I was with the body, and I was still not happy!

Backstage at a bodybuilding competition is a very interesting space. I am sure most men would die to be there with these incredible bikini-clad bodies everywhere you look! It is very surreal. We all look like overcooked turkeys at Christmas with the excessive fake tan and oil, which seems to smear on every available door, wall and hard surface. I do wonder about the poor cleaners who have to clean up after a show! We are all primping and pumping, ready for our callout. Everyone else looks relaxed and confident, and I am nearly peeing my pants with nerves and anxiety! Not to mention the hunger pains, the emotional rawness of barely eating for weeks and the insane training schedule of the week prior. Things have changed these days; but let me tell you we all may look like sex goddesses, but most of us feel like crap!

Not really the environment for the universe to send me a message; nonetheless, this is the time that I receive my calling. I can barely speak but feel that I need to chat to my fellow competitors to feel a little more secure going out on stage. One of the girls, who turns out to be the long-standing winner of our category, tells me she is studying to be a health coach through a college in New York. Huh? What is a health coach?

How I even remembered that conversation is a miracle in itself. When I came back down to the real world 24 hours later, I did remember this conversation and googled, which led me to the Institute of Integrative Nutrition®. Within a week I had enrolled in the year-long online course, and for the first time in 20 years I actually finished a course I started!

And here we are. ☺

Top Tips

- Make a list of all the things you simply love doing! What makes you smile? And I don't mean spending time with your loved ones. Something outside the human bonds of relationships. There is a career attached to everything these days; you just may not have heard of it. Now is the time to start utilising this wonderful tool called Google.
- Have a think about what you were good at in school or what you loved doing as a child. Were you obsessed with horses? Or loved

drawing? Childhood whims may not lead you to your passion as an adult, but they might. I can remember going through my surfer girl stage. Nope!

- Ask yourself, if money was limitless, what would you do?
- Take an inventory of your talents. What are you good at or have a natural aptitude for? I am not talking about what you are good at but don't like doing very much. I am talking about what you are good at that you enjoy!
- Take a closer look at who makes you annoyed or jealous. Is it because they are doing things in life that you would like to do? So often, particularly as women, we don't like someone (another woman), and the reason can be jealousy but we find it difficult to articulate. Who drives you mad? Maybe for completely different reasons, but it may be you want to live the life they are living!
- Find others who share your passion. Try the website Meetup, check out your local community college for a short course, volunteer and get to know people who are already in the field.
- Still struggling? Use your journal to write without an agenda. Inspiration and new ideas can come up unexpectedly when you write, and it might become easier to connect some dots.
- Go easy on yourself. We are all on a different spiritual journey; some of us find our passion later on in life, and the timing is perfect either way. And it doesn't have to be a career. If you have a hobby that lights your fire, that's great! Just make sure you find the time to do it regularly!
- Still need a hand? Read *The Passion Test* by Janet Bray Altwood & Chris Attwood.

Of all the topics I have covered in this book, I attribute this one for my life coming out of the darkness. I started bodybuilding for all the wrong reasons, and I stumbled across the answers to my life-long quest. I found myself in a world that is all about aesthetics. Ironic, isn't it?! But just goes to show that you can discover your passion when you aren't even looking! It also led to a new career, which is the most rewarding thing I have ever done in life. I am totally in love, and, yes, maybe even addicted to supporting and inspiring women to be their best.

Find your calling. Many experts will tell you that we all have special talents that are waiting to be discovered and put towards a worthy pursuit. We are all here for some unique purpose that will allow us to develop our highest human potential and add tremendous value to the lives of those around us. Finding your passion doesn't necessarily mean you need to make a job out of it. To me it means that if you spend time doing your passion, you will bring more of yourself in every other area of your life. Spending time to do what lights your fire will, without doubt, bring out the best in you. I promise you your life will change once you discover it.

"Follow your bliss and the universe will open doors for you where there were only walls."

—Joseph Campbell
Food Matters, FMTV

Mind Conclusion

Change is hard, really hard. When you are dealing with changing your mind, it is difficult to measure compared to weight and muscle loss or gain. It's hard to assess the starting point, your progress or even the end result. How can you change something when you can't even articulate what the issue is in the first place? As surprising as this might be, discovering I had low self-worth issues was a revelation to me. It is an issue that plagues too many women who are also stumbling along without this awareness. Insecurity will sabotage health and happiness every time and surfaces in every area of life. I look back on how I behaved, and it is all so clear to me now! But at the time I was blind. Having the strength to recognise and own this part of you, to take full responsibility for the state of your life, is vital for your health, happiness and success. I only discovered it by accident, by pursuing more vanity and by feeding my ego with my obsession of my appearance.

I hope that my journey has inspired you to assess your own life, and if anything has made you feel uncomfortable, I would encourage you to ask yourself why. I also hope that if you are striving for the perfect body, the attractive exterior, that my story also shows that having these things does not guarantee happiness. I would hazard a guess that I am not unique in the insecure, good-looking woman category. I found myself from the outside in, which is ironic and backward. The answer is from the inside, and once you master that, the outside won't matter so much. I promise!

Final Tip: Fall in love with the journey!

To incorporate every step I have taken in this book requires a massive amount of time and change. I would recommend only attempting one at a time! I certainly didn't adopt it all in one day or week, and so many of these steps have been percolating in my mind for many, many years!

When I look back on my journey and my success in bodybuilding and overcoming depression, my final tip has been derived from my love of the journey. Because it is not the end result that is my reward—I am not at the end! It is the person that I have become through this journey and the thorough enjoyment I get every single day.

We are so caught up in working towards a goal because we think when we get to the end we will be happy. While this may be true, if you are only fixated on the end, once you get there the happiness will be short-lived and will not bring you the deep satisfaction you thought you would get. I believe the true success of making and achieving goals is embracing the journey and the person you become throughout that journey. Whether you can see or feel the personal growth or not, it has occurred. So instead of just celebrating the end result, celebrate the journey. Celebrate the process. Celebrate the smallest step. Celebrate the self-discipline you exercise to get there. Celebrate the new strengths you have discovered in yourself. Celebrate the improved you!

My greatest reward in life is now supporting women in finding their inner goddess, to reconnect with that lost mojo, to discover the beautiful woman that is inside them regardless of their weight! Although I love supporting women in this, too! We all have a very special gift to share with the world, and it breaks my heart to see women waste their lives and happiness like I have. We all get there in our own time, and when the time is right for you, I would love to support you!

My half century is this year, and it will be my biggest and best year yet! Age truly is no barrier to your dreams; it is all in your mind!

"Happiness is not a finish line, and if we can't feel it amid the mess and striving, we might never feel it."

—Ben Saunders
Food Matters, FMTV

About the Author

Jane grew up in Melbourne, Australia with a middle-class background and is proudly a fifth generation Australian from English heritage. With a private school education in Melbourne and finishing in Canberra, she has enjoyed a successful corporate career as a Payroll Manager and is highly regarded in the payroll industry.

With depression being her close companion throughout her adult life, she has suffered with addictions, eating disorders, anxiety, heartache and insecurities. Having tried for many, many years to overcome her emotional issues, it wasn't until the age of 46 when she decided to compete as a fitness model that the pieces of the puzzle all fell into place. Through this intense journey to achieve the perfect female form and compete on stage, she inadvertently stumbled across the answers she had spent a life time searching for.

With the nutritional knowledge and personal development gained from her bodybuilding journey, Jane furthered her passion for nutrition and coaching by studying with the Institute of Integrative Nutrition® graduating in April 2014.

Jane resides in Sydney, Australia where she continues her bodybuilding and spiritual journey. Her commitment and discipline to her athlete's lifestyle for a woman her age is inspirational. She has devoted her life to not only achieving her own fitness goals but to spreading the ripple effect of health and wellness which she does through her influential example and her exclusive coaching program. More information can be found on her website: www.janecurnow.com.

Made in the USA
Lexington, KY
12 March 2018